D1596157

YOU DON'T GET TO QUIT

FAIL, YES. QUIT, NO.

TRACEY POWELL

MVHL

For permission requests, write to the publisher, addressed "Attention: Permissions Coordinator," carol@markvictorhansenlibrary.com

Quantity sales special discounts are available on quantity purchases by corporations, associations, and others. For details, contact the publisher at carol@markvictorhansenlibrary.com

Orders by U.S. trade bookstores and wholesalers. Email: carol@markvictorhansenlibrary.com

Creative contribution by Lisa Shiroff
Cover Design - Low & Joe Creative, Brea, CA 92821
Book Layout - DBree, StoneBear Design

Manufactured and printed in the United States of America distributed globally by markvictorhansenlibrary.com

New York | Los Angeles | London | Sydney

ISBN: 979-8-88581-059-3 Hardback
ISBN: 979-8-88581-060-9 Paperback
ISBN: 979-8-88581-061-6 eBook
Library of Congress Control Number: 2022916602

Contents

Dedication

This book is dedicated to my parents, Ivan Powell and Geraldine Greig, who individually and collectively have had an everlasting impact on my life perspective and individual trajectory. Both were artists and instilled an immense sense of appreciation for artistic expression and the value of reading, writing, and maintaining a home library.

To my father, for his trekking our family on adventures across North America, Mexico, and Western Europe. The greatest lesson he taught me was: "It doesn't matter what has happened or what anyone has done to you. The only thing that matters is, what are you going to do?" This principle still rings true as a reminder that we all have choices to make every day on how we think and what decisions we will make and what actions and directions we will take in lives.

To my mother, for her nurturing and discipline and for expanding my horizons, from swimming lessons and swim team to private school and classic educational upbringing. It has always been my mother who has celebrated my triumphs with me and provided an unwavering sense of support and encouragement in all situations, even when I failed. She has been my biggest fan.

A special shout-out goes to my sister, Alexis, and brother, Ivan, both of whom continue to provide me with their unique perspectives, candid feedback, and unwavering love and support.

And finally, a special thanks to my wife, Erica, for the years raising our two sons and holding down the home front while I forged a successful executive-level banking career to provide a comfortable lifestyle for our family.

Special Appreciation to DJ Nanda, Vice Dean for Faculty and Research, Miami Herbert Business School, who witnessed my failure during a project presentation, and instantly supported me through genuine coaching and encouragement. Through DJ's real-time support and encouragement, I gained a renewed sense of confidence and courage to refocus my efforts, and developed of an innovative, business application that solidified my standing as a thought leader in LATAM and global business innovation.

Prologue

Tanner and Marley are reeling from the devastating impact of having their parents killed in a freak car accident. Emotionally scared, they're left to pick up the pieces of their broken lives.

Their cousin, Joe, ends up building a small restaurant empire that is hugely successful, until he makes several miscalculations that bring his business empire crashing to the ground. Riddled with defeat, bankruptcy, and social humiliation, Joe wallows in his failure, which keeps his life in a stagnant holding pattern with little hope for the future.

Meanwhile, Cassie Davis is motivated to keep pushing forward with her career as a life coach and non-profit founder, after failing in her prior role working for the local municipality.

As our characters strive to create meaning and achieve success in their lives, circumstances allow their paths to cross, and they develop a dialogue of intrigue and suspense that forces each of them to dig deep within their souls to discover their true goals and motivations and uncover some of the fears and inhibitions that have been holding them back.

Welcome to this adventure as, together, we explore the paths that each of them take on a journey of self-reflection and internal motivation, as well as the principals they incorporate to achieve their respective goals and dreams.

CHAPTER 1

A MESSY SITUATION

It was a good thing Cassie knew she couldn't hold a note. Otherwise, she'd be belting out a tune as she strutted down the street, unaware that her crooning was scaring children and small animals. Instead of forcing her singing on the world, she showed her joy by beaming an uninhibited smile and nodding good morning to everyone she passed. *What a day!* Crisp autumn air filled the city with festive energy. The little trees lining the streets showed off their fall colors. The morning sun streamed at a slant, and everything glistened with a golden tint. In her opinion, the only thing that could make the day better was a good cup of coffee.

Ding! She dug her cell out from her shoulder bag and read Micki's text: "Break a leg!"

Cassie replied with a crossed-finger emoji, though she knew she made her own luck. Dog-on-a-bone perseverance had brought her to where she was, and she knew it would be what took her to the next level in her career. She was on her way to appear on a panel at the chamber of commerce—an opportunity that was a direct result of her steadfast focus on her goals. She was ready for it. Excited and eager to rub elbows with some of the most important business leaders in the area, she knew the event would do more than just solidify her as a reputable life coach. Even better, it would guide the local community in supporting the nonprofit she and Micki created. Yes! It was a great day.

Now, if she could just grab some coffee before she made it to the chamber of commerce building.

Tanner inhaled deeply as he stepped inside the café. Still no pumpkin spice. When were they going to change the menu for fall? Or was this the only place in town that wouldn't be offering pumpkin-spiced muffins with pumpkin-flavored coffee?

"Good morning, Tanner," the barista, Evan, said as soon as he spotted him. "One light-and-sweet coming up."

Joe was near the back of the dining area, standing with his hands on his hips, looking at the floor. Tanner could hear him muttering and complaining even from afar. He eyed up the granola bars and dried-fruit clusters and took a pass. Nothing looked good enough to make it worth postponing talking to his cousin. He headed toward the back.

"Good morning, Joe."

"Ah, if it isn't the Clark family problem solver." Joe popped open a slippery-when-wet sign and placed it between them. "Haven't seen you in a couple of days. Was kind of hoping you'd given up on me."

"Believe it or not, I come here because the coffee is good."

Joe gave him a sideways look and smirked. "I hope you don't play poker."

"I don't, but why?"

"You're not good at bluffing." Joe sprayed cleaner over a mess on the floor.

"Okay, how about the coffee is good, *and* I care about you? The whole family cares about you." Tanner leaned back on his heels and hoped his grin didn't look like a used-car salesman's. "But Marley does need you to move out of her basement."

"You think I don't know that?" Joe used a squeegee to push the messy gunk onto a dustpan. "I'll talk to her tonight. I just need a couple more weeks at this gig. Then I'll have enough money to move into my own place."

Joe had been saying "a couple more weeks" for so long that Tanner suspected it had become a sort of mantra for him—one that kept him stuck where he was no matter how much time passed. Inevitably, something would happen that would require another "couple more weeks": his bicycle was stolen, and he had to save for a new one; he chipped a tooth, and the repair wasn't covered by insurance; he'd been scratched by a cat and missed several days of work watching for cat-scratch fever symptoms.

But it wasn't just a matter of Joe finding the funds to move out. Joe needed to find a better job, one that would enable him to live a better life. Tanner couldn't understand why his cousin didn't seem to want that. He and Joe were the same age, but Joe looked at least ten years older. At one time, Joe had been proud, fit, and well-dressed, but the man before Tanner now wore beat-up jeans cinched with a belt under a growing muffin-top belly. His T-shirt was stained, and he stooped now, even when he wasn't bent over cleaning up someone else's mess. In fact, Joe's hunched shoulders and protruding stomach gave him the appearance of a seahorse.

"See this?" Joe's growl snapped Tanner back to attention. He pointed to the floor where bits of the mess appeared cemented in place. "That's oatmeal with ground flax, chia seeds, and honey."

"Sounds, um, healthy." Tanner couldn't help but grimace.

"I'm sure it is if you can get it down your gullet. Why that woman insists on creating concoctions like that instead of giving people what they really want, I haven't a clue." Joe knelt to use a scraper on the dried-on food.

"See? That's why you need to get out there again. No one knows restaurants like you do. Have you—"

"Don't start in on me, Tanner." Joe kept his eyes

focused on the floor as he sprayed more cleaning solution. "I'll talk to your sister tonight, so you can put your nose in someone else's business. I'll move out of her basement as soon as I can." He pulled out a rag, turned his back toward Tanner, and continued cleaning without looking up.

Tanner got the hint: his cousin wasn't open to any more conversation.

"Okay." He blew out a sigh. "But, you know, anytime you do want to get back out there, I'm here to help with the resume, connect you with people—whatever you need."

"Yeah, yeah, yeah. I know. Heard you say that before." Joe stood with a grunt, picked up his tools and cleaner, and walked away without another word.

Yeah, yeah, yeah. If he had heard and really did know, why wasn't he doing anything about it? Joe was brilliant. He'd had such a fantastic career as a restaurateur. Sure, he'd lost it all because of a couple of questionable business deals. But didn't he want to stage a comeback? Didn't he prefer living the high life he'd once had over crashing on a beat-up couch in someone's basement?

Tanner returned to the front, picked up the cup with his name, cheered Evan to thank him, turned around, and slammed into a woman.

"Oh no!"

His coffee splashed everywhere, but for a heartbeat,

Tanner was motionless. The woman he had run into had the most amazing brown eyes he'd ever seen.

"This is going to stain!" She shook out the hem of her cardigan.

"I'm so sorry. I was lost in thought." Tanner handed her a wad of napkins. "Just blot it. Don't rub. Rubbing will force it deeper into the cloth."

"So, you're a laundry expert." She began dabbing at the stain. "Lucky me. I bumped into the right guy."

"Hey, I'm just trying to help." Tanner dropped to his knees and mopped up the floor with another handful of napkins. The last thing he wanted was for Joe to come out and see who'd made the latest mess.

"I'm sure you are. I'm sorry." She paused to inspect her sweater. "This just isn't the best day to be wearing coffee."

"I don't suppose . . . " Tanner didn't finish his sentence. The woman had already turned and was back out the door. He had been hoping to buy a fresh cup of coffee for her. Well, if she was here today, maybe she'd be back again some other time. Tanner knew he'd be back to talk to Joe—frequently. Maybe he'd be able to run into her and her brown eyes again. Well, not literally the next time, of course.

###

"Can I have your name please?" a volunteer asked when Cassie approached the check-in table.

"Cassie Davis."

The volunteer looked at an iPad and tapped it. "Oh, you're a presenter." She twisted around to retrieve a folder. "Here's a little info on everyone else on the panel and a few questions we already have lined up before we start taking them from the audience."

"Great, thank you."

"Please look over your bio as soon as possible and let us know if we need to announce any changes at the beginning of the program. Let's see . . . " She paused as she looked at the iPad again. "Looks like you will be seated—"

"Sweetheart!" A booming, raspy female voice startled Cassie. "Britney! You look gorgeous, honey. Just gorge!" A woman in a narrow black skirt and vibrant red silk shirt was suddenly in front of her. She leaned over the table to pull the volunteer, who Cassie gathered was Britney, up into an awkward hug.

"Thanks, Gabi. I'll get your info in just a sec." Over the woman's shoulder, Britney raised her eyebrows. Cassie smiled back. If nothing else, she admired the woman in red's exuberance.

As soon as she was released, Britney continued. "Cassie, you'll be in the second chair on the left side of the panel table." She pointed, and Cassie headed over, eager to look at those questions.

She took her seat and did as told: scanned her bio, which seemed fine, then focused on the questions to strategize what she'd like to say for each. She preferred to improv in situations like this so she could be more genuine. But knowing what they were going to ask helped soothe her jittery nerves. She had been on top of the world until she'd had coffee spilled all down her front at the café. Now she needed to focus and get back into the confident zone again.

She became so absorbed in her thoughts that she almost didn't hear a man speaking next to her.

"I hope you're not the vengeful type," he said.

"What?" Cassie asked. It was the guy who'd spilled the coffee down her cardigan, which she'd had to drop off at the cleaners on the way. Blotting had not quite worked.

"I said I hope you're not the vengeful type," he repeated, smiling at her.

"Not usually." Cassie grinned as he took the last seat on the panel. "At least not when there's an audience present. You'll be safe as long as this panel lasts."

"Ha!" He had an easy, friendly smile when he laughed. "I'm so sorry. Did the stain come out?"

"Let's just say you should take 'laundry expert' off your resume. But the folks at the cleaners said they could get it out."

"Yikes. I really am sorry. Send me your bill. I'm happy to reimburse you." He handed her a card.

"Tanner Clark?"

"That would be me."

"I am so glad you spilled coffee on me." So, this was her lucky day. Tanner was a local celebrity of sorts. Not only was he a motivational speaker who worked with large corporations, but he often emceed fundraisers. It'd be amazing to have him connected with her nonprofit. "You don't have to pay for my dry cleaning, but I'd like to talk to you about something."

"Ask away." He leaned back in his chair with such a charming grin, Cassie almost forgot what she wanted to discuss. Almost.

"Well, I have a nonprofit that—"

"Sweetheart!" The woman with the loud, raspy voice seemed to have followed Cassie. "I was so excited when I saw your name on the docket. How've you been?" She ripped Tanner out of his chair and pulled him into a hug. Like Britney, he bugged his eyes at Cassie over her shoulder. "Oh! Have I got something for you, Tanner! Been working on a new plan. Let's catch up after this is over!"

"I'd love to hear what you have going on, Gabi," he said when she let go of him. "But I'm afraid I'm booked up over the next couple of months."

"You'll be glad you spoke to me." She poked him with a finger hard enough that his shoulder jerked back. "It's going to be big—big!"

"I'm sure. Everything you do is big."

"Just like my hair! Ha!" She clapped her hands together so loudly Cassie jumped in her seat. "Sweetheart!" she yelled as she tore across the stage.

"Whew!" was all Cassie could say at first. She blinked a few times while her heart rate resumed its regular cadence. "She's certainly . . . something."

"Yep." Tanner returned to his seat. "That's Gabi Gold. Most consider her a bit much. You know how life coaches can be."

"I do, actually." What did that mean? Was that woman really a life coach? Cassie scanned the info sheets and found her bio.

> **Gabi Gold is the founder of Gold Coaching Solutions, where she takes self-love to a whole new level. She's the author of the *I Love Me!* series of self-help books and host of the Gold Lovin' podcast. Gabi specializes in teaching self-love because, 'If you can love yourself, you can love anybody.'**

Cassie hoped the last sentence was a misprint.

"So, I think you were about to introduce yourself." Tanner tapped her arm.

"Oh, I'm Cassie Davis." She grinned at him. She could lead with the nonprofit, but she suddenly felt a bit mischievous. Cassie wanted to see how he'd react to her job title. "I'm a life coach with Davis Life Solutions."

A life coach? Well, that was disappointing. Tanner couldn't believe the chamber would have two on one panel. Granted, Gabi was there because she managed to get on every panel everywhere. But had Gabi ever been able to help anyone but herself? She only annoyed Joe when Tanner had hired her to work with him. Life coaches were limited in their abilities, to say the least. Not at all effective, in his experience. He was so disappointed. Cassie had such lovely eyes.

"I'd like to begin today's panel with a hearty 'thank you' to our sponsors." Garret Fagan, the facilitator, spoke into a microphone. "In particular, Alice Bradshaw, CEO of Digital Access Solutions. Not only did she sponsor today's event, but it was because of her team's effort that we had such a smooth check-in process."

"Sweetheart!" Out of the corner of Tanner's eye, he saw Cassie jump in her seat. "We need to talk!"

"Right," Garret continued. "So, let's get started." Garrett introduced each of the five speakers. "We already surveyed chamber members and everyone in the audience—who should be a chamber member by the way—and put together a few questions that seemed to hit lots of hot buttons. We'll start with those, then take additional questions from the floor. Are we ready?"

"Always!" Gabi boomed.

Cassie flinched.

Tanner suppressed a laugh.

"You can begin with me, sweetheart!"

"We'll start at the end and go down the row," Garret explained. "On the next question, the second person will be first to answer."

"Got it!" Gabi shouted. "Spread the love!"

Cassie scribbled a note on the bottom of the program and slid it in front of Tanner: I think I had too much caffeine today.

He pulled out a pen and scribbled back: Nah. Gabi has that effect on people.

"Let's talk about failure." Garrett faced the panel. "What advice do you have when you've set a business goal, created a logical plan to attain it, but you fail? Do you create a new goal or a new plan? How do you get over fear of failure? Let's begin with you," pointing to one of the panelists.

He answered the way Tanner expected: he spoke about the need to ensure goals align with the company mission and objectives, then he suggested they seek guidance from a superior. Tanner agreed, but was disappointed.

Isn't that just common sense? he wrote to Cassie.

She scribbled back: *Something innovative and original would be more helpful.*

Tanner nodded at her words. Okay, so maybe this one life coach has a good idea or two.

"Just give yourself applause," Gabi spoke second. "That's what I do. When I mess something up—ha! And, boy, do I mess things up!" She slammed her hand on the table. Cassie, startled, dropped her pen. "I just start clapping. Because for everything I do wrong, there's something I do right. And clapping makes me feel better."

There was a pause, as if Garrett were waiting for more from her. Cassie picked up her pen and wrote: *At least that's something innovative.*

Oh, man! Did that mean Cassie agreed with whatever point Gabi was trying to make? He really wanted to like this woman. But a life coach?

After a moment of silence, Garret moved on to Jenna, a leader of a small tech group in the area who spoke about SMART goals. Tanner inwardly groaned. Sure, SMART goals sounded great—specific, measurable, attainable, relevant, and time-based parameters could be very helpful—but they didn't allow for flexibility and they rarely inspired creativity.

Ah, Cassie's turn. He listened intently.

"I think we all need to remember that failure can be a pathway to success, but only if we let it. Failure offers us an opportunity to learn and grow. With each failure, we're given a chance to correct our course, to analyze what went wrong so we can do something different, and then get back on the path to success. The key to doing that is not to beat yourself up for failing. That's a surefire way to stay derailed from reaching your goal, which I think is what Gabi was saying. Accept that you're human, which means you'll mess up on occasion. But remember, messing up isn't really failing. Not learning from your mistakes and letting them sideline you from moving forward—that's what quitting looks like."

"So, is failure a choice?" Tanner asked.

"I'm saying it's just a moment in time. What happens next is up to you."

"Interesting." Tanner nodded. "Impressive idea, but where does motivation come in? That's the crux of the issue, right? When setting a goal and making a plan, we need to think about how we'll monitor our motivation as we move along with it. As Zig Ziglar once said, 'People often say motivation doesn't last. Well, neither does bathing, that's why we recommend it every day.'"

CHAPTER 2

MAKING CONNECTIONS

Cassie took notes on different people she wanted to speak to throughout the event. She'd placed a star by Alice Bradshaw. If she connected with only Alice, she'd be ecstatic.

"You have some interesting ideas." Tanner stood with Cassie after the discussion wrapped.

"Even for a life coach?" she teased.

"Perhaps I was a bit hasty in my judgment. It's just that, in my experience, life coaches really aren't beneficial."

"Thank you, sweetheart!" Gabi roared. Before Cassie got her bearings, Gabi tugged her into a hug. "Women supporting women! You understand! You go, boss lady!" She released her. "And listen! If you need help getting your business up and running, I'd be happy to consult for you. I'll even give you a discount on my services."

"Great." Cassie reached for something to say. "I appreciate the offer, but—"

"Alice! Sweetheart! We need to talk!" Gabi let go of Cassie and trotted off toward the audience.

Cassie regained her footing. "Oh, I need to speak

with Alice Bradshaw, too." Cassie watched Gabi slam the woman into a hug.

"I don't think Alice needs a life coach."

There was a tone in Tanner's voice that was a little off-putting. Was he disparaging her? "You know, some of the most successful people in the world have a life coach on speed dial. But that doesn't matter right now. That's not what I wanted to talk to Alice Bradshaw about." She picked her bag up off the back of her chair and rummaged through it until she found a business card. "Here. I run the Making Connections nonprofit. We create mentorship connections for people in need of job skills. I think Alice's company would be a great resource for us."

Cassie glanced over the audience. Alice was scampering toward the door as if trying to escape the room. "But I don't think that will happen today. Shoot!" Cassie watched the woman speed through the exit with Gabi close on her heels in her blazing red shirt.

"You still got me." Tanner opened his arms wide.

Cassie raised her eyebrows at him, curious what he meant.

"I happen to have an 'in' with Alice."

"You do?"

"Her group's productivity skyrocketed after I led some team-building and motivational workshops with them. She always takes my call." He glanced at Cassie's business card. "I'll introduce you two by email. I'm sure Alice will want to help."

###

"Good news!" Cassie announced as soon as she entered her office.

"Cool! But let me get this call first." Micki clicked on her headset. "Thank you for calling Making Connections. How can I help you?" She dug through the piles of paper on her desk until she found a pencil. Within seconds, she dropped it and rolled her eyes at Cassie. "I'm sorry. That's just not what we do. We're not a dating service." She hung up. "We gave ourselves the wrong name."

"We'll become so successful and well known there will be no confusion." Cassie sat in the chair opposite Micki.

"I love that you practice the same positivity you preach. But I still think we should have thought more about the name. Anyway, what's the good news?"

"The panel went really well. I spoke to a few companies afterward, and two more have agreed to host tables at our career fair."

"Awesome!" Micki shuffled around the piles on her desk again until she found a steno pad. "Who are they?" Another call came in. "Wait!" She clicked through. "Thank you for calling Making Connections."

Cassie took the pad and wrote down the information for Micki.

The caller on the other end of the line had absorbed Micki's attention. Cassie listened to her repeated, "uh huh," "really?" and "that's so interesting" and wished she could hear the other end of the conversation.

"Well, I'd love to help you. I really would. You sound amazing." Micki smirked at Cassie. "But we're not a dating service, hon." She clicked off and giggled. "He sounded cute. I was just about to get his name for you, but then he said he didn't like dogs. What kind of man doesn't like dogs?"

"Ones with allergies?"

"Maybe. But you know, perhaps all these calls for a dating service will help us find you Mr. Right."

"I'm too busy for a Mr. Anybody right now." Cassie handed her the notepad. "In fact, *we* may be too busy. I also connected with someone who has an in with Alice Bradshaw of Digital Access Solutions."

"She—they—would be perfect!" Micki rummaged through her desk, spun in her chair, and then pulled out an accordion folder from under a pile of manila files on the credenza behind her. "Look what I found in the office supply store this morning. Who knew there were so many ways to organize information without a computer?"

Cassie adopted a deadpan face. "Millions of people were in business for centuries before computers."

"Whatever. I've labeled a slot for each company we want to connect with, including DAS. These are my notes and everything I've printed out from my home computer that will one day go into this new computer when we no longer use it as a plant stand." She nodded at the potted blooming begonia sitting on the dead desktop computer tower. "I have a full dossier on Alice Bradshaw. You do realize, don't you, that her company is so big, she could overwhelm us?"

"That would be an awesome problem to have, though, wouldn't it?"

"Do you ever take off those rose-tinted glasses?"

"Why would I?"

"That's why I love you. When are you talking to her?"

"I don't know." Cassie pulled her phone from her attaché case. "The craziest thing happened this morning. I was getting coffee at that cute little café down the street, and some man bumped into me. Spilled his coffee all over the place, including on my cardigan."

"Did it stain?"

"I took it to the cleaners." Cassie shrugged. "Anyway, he wound up sitting next to me on the panel." She clicked on her email icon and scrolled through. Wonderful! Tanner Clark had kept his word.

"What's that smile on your face about?"

"He knows Alice Bradshaw and promised to connect

us." She held her phone out to Micki. "And he kept his word."

"Seems to me that smile has nothing to do with Alice Bradshaw."

"Two more weeks?" Marley tilted her head as she snipped the bottom leaves from a rose stem. "He— you both—said 'two weeks' when he moved in down there. He's been couch surfing in my basement for three months now, Tanner."

"I know. Look, if I had a bigger place, I'd take him in."

"And if he's going to stay with me much longer, I'm going to need a bigger place!" She pointed to her belly. "Don't forget, you have another niece or nephew coming in April."

"I haven't forgotten." He wandered through rows of irises, occasionally picking one up, then returning it. "And I'm hoping for a nephew, by the way."

"I'm aware. I think you've mentioned it about three dozen times since Dylan and I made the announcement last week."

Tanner turned up a different row and began poking through containers of carnations. He wanted something small and not conspicuously flirty that he could send to Cassie. "What's good for an apology?"

"You can't send me flowers, Tanner. I own the shop." Marley bopped him with a rose before poking it into the arrangement she was working on. "But that's a nice gesture."

"What is?"

"Offering me flowers as an apology."

"What do I owe you an apology for?"

"It's your fault Joe thinks he can live in my basement indefinitely." She twisted the vase around, looking at it from various perspectives, then shoved it aside. "Look. I'm not trying to be unkind. But I'm running out of patience. The room Charlotte and Emily use as a play-room is this little one's future bedroom." She rubbed her belly. "Dylan and I need to get the basement cleared out, painted, and re-carpeted. I'd like to get new furniture down there too. Which means Joe has to go."

"I get it. You're due in April. So, how soon do you need him out?" He picked up a basket of yellow daisies.

"What is he waiting for anyway?"

"The funds for an apartment."

"Hasn't he been waiting for them long enough?" Marley sighed. "Was that mean?"

"A little. But I get where you're coming from. I really do, and I'm working on it." He held the daisies out at arm's length. "How's this for an apology?"

"I don't know." Marley twisted her mouth and squinted at him. "What did you do?"

"I spilled coffee on her sweater, and then I insulted her profession."

"Oh my. Who is she?"

"Someone with very pretty eyes."

"Then level up. Get tulips."

CHAPTER 3

ANOTHER ~~MANIC~~ MOTIVATED MONDAY

C assie added water to the vase of yellow tulips from Tanner on her desk. She still wasn't sure what to think about them. Such a lovely gesture, but for a little coffee on her cardigan? Granted, it was an organic cotton, cream-colored cardigan, and the stain had made the dry cleaner cringe. But still. The introduction to Alice was enough.

Did he have other intentions? Did she want him to have other intentions?

No. She didn't have time for thoughts like that. Besides, he obviously didn't take her career seriously. How could she be interested in a man who thought she was a flake?

She double-checked her reflection in the mirror. Today was another exciting opportunity for her—and for her career. Thankfully, the local TV station didn't share Tanner's opinion of life coaches. They had asked her to audition to be the voice of their Monday Motivation segment on their morning news show. Of course, she agreed. But what to wear?

She was on her third outfit that morning: a black mock turtleneck sweater and black-and-white striped palazzo pants. Yes, this looked appropriate. Professional, yet not too serious. Approachable, friendly. Her light chestnut hair fell in a wave just past her shoulders. Should she pin it back? Oh, maybe she could tuck a yellow tulip behind her ear. Or would that come off as silly? Maybe she'd save something like that for after she landed the gig. Dry runs are never a good time for experimentation. Or were they? Should she be more daring in what she wore? Make a statement?

The happy-anticipation butterflies in her stomach turned into fearful moths. A glance at the clock assured her she had a few minutes to get control of her brain so she could get to the station in the right mindset.

She grabbed the journal from her nightstand and sat in her comfy chair by the window. In the back of the journal, she found the folded slip of paper with her seven essential questions. She had the questions memorized, but she found it helpful to slow herself down and read through them from time to time. It helped her process and think.

1. What emotion are you feeling and why? Cassie closed her eyes and took three long breaths. *Anxious.*

2. What thoughts are behind the emotion? *I'm afraid that the people at the station will judge me and decide I'm not worthy of the weekly spot if I don't fulfill their expectations perfectly. What if my appearance is off? Or they don't like my message? Then they won't offer the position to me.*

3. Are there truths in the thoughts? *No. The thoughts are all speculation.*

4. If there are truths in the thoughts, what action can you take now to resolve or soothe the emotion? If there are no truths in the thoughts, and because feelings are a result of our thoughts, what truths can lead you to a better feeling? *This anxiety is all mine—I created it. So, I can create the opposite. I can get control of how I think about the situation. I have no control over what goes on in anyone else's head, so worrying about what the people at the station think isn't doing me any good. Focusing on what I think will help me. What to think? How do I want to feel? I want to feel confident, sure, and certain.*

She closed her eyes again, took more deep breaths, and repeated those words silently in her head: confident, sure, and certain. *Feeling confident, sure, and certain means my body is relaxed. I can smile easily. It means I trust myself, and I trust my judgment. And that is a truth: I do trust myself and my judgment. I think I look good in this outfit. Not only do I think I look good in this outfit, but I know my message is one this community needs. People are open to receiving it. I have helped many people find the inner strength to follow through on their dreams, to make positive change in their lives. I am really good at what I do. So, I look good, and I am good!*

5. What's the worst that can happen in this situation? *That I won't get the weekly gig.*

6. And then what will you do? Cassie tapped the pen against her chin as she thought about it. *What will happen if I don't get this weekly spot? I'll find something else to do with my Monday mornings.*

7. What positive outcome can result from the worst that can happen in this situation? *More restful Sunday nights.*

Cassie realized she was grinning, and the anxiety had subsided. She loved this exercise.

Was that Cassie Davis? Tanner did a double take as he passed the glass wall. It was her! What on earth was she doing at the studio? He'd just finished recording thirty-second ads for his Thursday Pick-Me-Up segment and was on his way to see Joe again. But hanging around the studio for a little while to wait for Cassie seemed like a pleasant diversion.

He took a seat at the end of the hall, intending to relish the peace and quiet of the moment. But his sister still had sibling ESP and, as always, knew when it was the right time to be annoying. No sooner had he sat down than his phone dinged with a message from Marley.

Seriously?

Before he could respond, she sent a photograph. Tanner squinted at the image, unsure of what he was looking at. It was a room with light-beige walls and dark-brown carpeting—maybe. It was hard to tell. So much clothing was strewn all over the place, that he could barely see the floor. Also scattered about the place were to-go cups from the café where Joe worked.

It was Marley's basement.

I'm talking to him in a few minutes, Tanner assured her in a text.

Not talking. You're convincing him to move, Marley corrected.

What was he going to do?

The door to the recording studio opened. Phil, one of the producers, came out first and held it ajar. "Great job, Cassie!" he said. "You are definitely going to be the face of motivation around here."

"Hey! I thought I was the face of motivation around here." Tanner stood up.

Phil laughed. "I stand corrected. Cassie, you will be the face of Monday motivation, and Tanner here will remain the face of Thursday."

"Welcome to the team, Cassie." Tanner bowed.

"Thank you." She beamed the most beautiful smile. "And thank you, Phil. I'm so excited to be here."

"We're excited to have you." Phil led the way down the hall to the open reception area. "I'll let HR know. They'll reach out to you, probably later today, and arrange your onboarding. I'd like to have you start next Monday if that works for you?"

"Of course!" Her excitement was palpable.

"Congratulations." Tanner held the door open to leave the building.

"Thank you." Cassie stepped outside and waited for him. "I guess I should be embarrassed to say I didn't realize you were here on Thursdays."

"I just started last week. But I suppose I'll have to stay on my toes. I can see you easily failing your way into taking over my spot."

Cassie stopped on the sidewalk and turned to face him. She cocked her head to the side. "You know, I was almost about to thank you again for the beautiful flowers. But right now, I don't know what to think. It sounds like you're making fun of me."

"I'm not making fun of you." He made the sign of the cross across his chest. "Honest."

"Then you're making fun of my profession."

"I'm . . . look, the only other life coach I know is Gabi." His phone dinged. He had a feeling it was Marley and wanted to ignore it, but knew better. "I think this is my sister. Excuse me." A glance at his phone assured him he was right—another photo of the messy basement.

Heading over now, he typed and slid the phone back into his pocket.

"I'm not Gabi. But, for the record, I think she has a good message hidden behind all the flash."

"It must be hidden deep."

"Wow." Cassie raised her eyebrows and turned away. She began walking again.

Tanner felt like a schoolboy caught reading comics hidden inside his math book. He ran a few steps to catch up with her. "So, what's Gabi's message?"

"She's all about self-reliance and self-worth —self-love."

His phone dinged. He ignored it this time. "If that's what she's teaching, she's not doing a good job with it."

"I'll give you that. Her style is a bit over the top."

His phone dinged again. "Look." He stopped walking and waited. She stopped, too, and stood with arms crossed. He turned the phone, so she could see the screen.

"What is that mess?" she asked.

"My cousin Joe's life."

"What?"

"Not everyone is able to absorb their failures and hop back on the success path in life. Some people get so stuck, they become immobilized."

"Everyone can find their way out of a dark place." Cassie sounded like she believed what she said.

"That's what Gabi told him. Then her self-lovefest resulted in him getting demoted. He was making coffee at a café; now he's cleaning it up." He tapped her crossed arms with his phone. "Help me. I'm heading over to talk to him now. Me. You're the motivational guru around here. I talk to him probably three times a week. Each time I fail. How do I find success with my failures?"

"You learn from them and take a different approach informed by what you learned."

She said it like it was so simple to do. He shook his head. "I think there's no way Joe is turning his life around at this point."

"How do you motivate people if phrases like 'there's no way' come out of your mouth?"

"And if I say, 'there's certainly a way,' one will magically appear?"

"No. But at least you wouldn't be arguing for your limitations."

"I'm not arguing for anything. I'm just facing the facts."

"Facts? Tell me these facts."

He led her down a side street lined with small mom-and-pop stores. Double doors were wide open, with goods spilled out onto the sidewalk among cornstalks, hay bales, and pumpkins. As they walked, Tanner relished the pumpkin-spice smell and wished the café sold muffins once again. "Joe used to be super successful," he explained. "Remember the Victory Heights Restaurant?"

"Of course."

"That was one of his places. He's Joe Clark of Clark Enterprises."

Cassie stopped at a crosswalk and placed a hand on her chin.

"You must be remembering the headlines," Tanner said.

"I'm not sure what I'm remembering. He went belly up, right?"

"Right. Joe was crushed, personally, financially, professionally. He hit bottom and was on the verge of becoming homeless. I convinced my sister to let him bunk on a couch in her basement for a couple of weeks to give him a chance to get back on his feet."

"Why didn't you take him in?"

They crossed the street.

"My place is as big as a squirrel's nest. And that's not arguing for a limitation. There's barely room on my bathroom sink for one toothbrush."

She giggled.

What a delightful sound, Tanner thought. "Well, it's been over three months now. My sister is expecting another baby and needs that space. She's too nice to be forceful with him."

"I mean, she shouldn't have to. It was your idea to begin with."

"Sounds like you've been talking to my sister." He grinned. "So, coach, what do I tell him?"

"First, he has to be the one to want to move out. So, you need to learn what's motivating him to stay. And, frankly, this is something where Gabi's philosophy might help."

He stopped outside the café and faced her. "Are you intentionally trying to make me roll my eyes?"

She rolled hers. "He obviously doesn't feel worthy of the height of success he had before. He probably doesn't have the self-worth to achieve anything at this point." She appeared to mock Gabi by poking her finger into his shoulder, but she was much gentler. "You have to help him find that."

"Is there a map to the location?"

"It's in his failure."

"That again." Just when she looked so cute with the wind blowing her hair back from her face. He put his hands on his hips. "Do you seriously think people can fail their way to success?"

"Absolutely!"

"Even Joe? Someone who has experienced such a massive failure?" She obviously had no idea what kind of man his cousin was.

"Look, Mr. Motivation, failure is just a moment in time. How long it lasts is up to the individual."

"But doesn't the individual have to want to make a comeback?"

"Nobody truly wants to live as a shadow of their best self."

"I bet Joe does."

"I bet he doesn't."

"Oh, yeah?" Tanner took her hand and shook it. If she really could do something, he wanted to see it. "You're on."

"What?"

"I'll introduce you to him. How long do you think it will take for you to turn his life around and get him out of the shadows?"

"I usually work with people for six months."

"Okay." Tanner counted out the months. Marley was due in April—seven months away. That would only leave a month to paint and furnish the basement before the baby arrived, but he would help Dylan make it happen. "Okay, how much do you want to bet me that six months from now, you'll have helped Joe reclaim his career?"

"I don't know about this. I'm not one for gambling."

"It's just for fun. If you win, I pay you your six month's coaching fees. If I win, you . . . " he pursed his lips. He wanted to say she'd owe him a dinner date, but would she balk at that? Maybe he should step it back a little. "You buy me a cup of coffee."

"A cup of coffee? That I'm not going to have to buy because there's no way you're right about this. Deal."

CHAPTER 4

WRONG IMPRESSIONS

Cassie was a little surprised to discover that Joe worked at the coffee shop where she and Tanner first met—what a fateful spill! At least the coffee was good, although the pastries sounded a little too healthy to be called pastries.

"Plain-black, dark-roast, please," she told the barista.

"Really?" Tanner's eyes were somehow very wide as he frowned.

"Really. How do you take yours?"

"Sweet and light," the barista said. "Right, Tanner?"

"Right, Evan." Tanner's face reddened. "Um, thanks for remembering."

"Sweet and light, huh?" Cassie teased. "So, you're not a real coffee drinker, then?"

"Does dark and bitter mean you're a pro?"

"There's no one right way to drink coffee," Evan chimed in.

"I was just teasing," Cassie giggled, a light feeling washing over her, followed immediately by caution. She enjoyed being around Tanner, but she didn't want to. How could she enjoy being with someone who didn't take her career seriously? She couldn't be friends—or anything else—with someone who didn't respect her.

Tanner tried to shift the conversation into more casual topics. "So, when you're not coaching people, what do you do?"

"Well, I have another enterprise."

Not exactly what Tanner was looking for, but he'd go with it. "Oh, right. The nonprofit?"

So he remembered. "I used to be the director of the city's workforce development program."

"Really?" When he met her eyes, there seemed to be a new level of esteem on his face.

"Really. People often came to us for specific work because they were interested in certain industries, and they didn't necessarily always match up with their abilities and skills and experience. That old adage about how do you get experience if you can't get the job and how do you get the job if you don't have experience was playing out so frequently. It was so disheartening seeing smart, hardworking people intrigued by a particular career path that, because of various circumstances, was essentially closed off to them. I saw a need that the city's program couldn't fulfill, so I decided to start a nonprofit to help people be mentored into new professions."

"That's impressive. You're doing it all by yourself?" Yes, he was definitely looking at her with more respect.

"Pretty much. My friend Micki came on board to help me. She is a freelance writer who creates materials for PR and marketing firms, so she's excellent with the communications. But she's also great administrative support, which I really need. You have no idea how many people have been asking for our help, especially people who want to improve their tech skills. That's why I was so excited to connect with Alice Bradshaw. Her firm is the perfect place to find mentors."

"I'm glad I was able to help. Is there anything else I can do? Sounds like an amazing program."

"Well, we do have a career fair coming up. I think it would be awesome to have a motivational speaker present to our crowd. What do you think?"

"Send me the date, and I'll make it happen." He nodded toward the counter. "Our coffee is ready. Let me introduce you to Joe."

They took their cups, found a table outside, and Tanner went to find his cousin. Cassie sipped her brew and watched an employee from the boutique next door arrange pumpkins and hay bales near their entrance. She loved fall. Especially all the fall goodies. Maybe she could find some pumpkin-spiced muffins to take back to the shop.

"Here she is," Tanner's voice startled her. "Cassie, this is my cousin, Joe. Joe, meet Cassie Davis."

"Hi, Joe." Cassie waved to the chair opposite her. "Do you have a minute to sit down?"

Joe narrowed his eyes at Tanner and took the seat.

"Great. Well, I'll see you both soon." Tanner walked away.

Cassie furrowed her brow and watched him leave the two of them behind. She had expected more of an introduction from Tanner. Or at least a proper goodbye. But she needed to shift her focus from Tanner to Joe. Meeting and getting to know new clients was one of her favorite parts of this job, after all.

"Sorry about my appearance." Joe gestured toward his clothes. "I wasn't expecting this."

"No problem. I never judge a book by its cover." Cassie waved her hand. "So, tell me about yourself, Joe."

He froze, a mixture of suspicion and apprehension clouding his face.

"Start anywhere." Cassie leaned back in her chair to encourage him to do likewise and relax a little. "Tell me anything about you."

He ducked his head, looked at the table. "There's not a lot to tell anymore. I love food. I love to cook and experiment with recipes."

"Nice. So do you cook often?"

"I, um, well, no. Not lately, anyway."

"I see. And you work here?"

"Right. For the past couple of months. It's just an interim place for me."

"Interim—that's a great way to look at your current situation." See there? Joe was already proving Tanner wrong. He wanted out of the shadows. "So, what's next for you?"

"I'm still figuring that out."

"What do you do for fun?"

He finally leaned back in his chair. "I'm sorry. This just feels a little awkward. It's been a while since I talked about myself, especially to an attractive woman. Tanner kind of sprung this on me, so I'm really sorry."

"There's nothing to apologize for—and thank you, by the way. But let's just focus on you. Just share the real Joe with me. How does that sound?"

He tilted his head back and laughed. "The 'real' Joe? I don't know if that's a good idea. Here's the summary: I had a big business for a while. I hit a rough patch, and now I'm here."

"Why here?"

"Well, a coffee shop felt like a good way to ease myself back into the industry. I've always been good in the kitchen. I've only ever focused on that in my life. I suppose because I'd never found the right woman yet." He cocked his head to the side and winked.

At least she thought he winked. Maybe something flew in his eye, or perhaps it was a nervous twitch?

"So, you know how that goes, right? You haven't found the right person either, huh?"

"I've been busy with my career." Cassie's cheeks warmed. So, it was a wink. This was not the foot she was hoping to get started on. "You had a successful business, now you don't. You're probably not working as many hours as you used to. What do you do in your spare time?"

"Lately, I've been taking it easy. I used to work out quite a bit. Actually, I should get back into that. Do you go to a gym?"

"I do. I make taking care of my health a priority. So—"

"Where do you go? Maybe we could work out together?"

"I practice yoga, but that doesn't seem like your type of activity." Cassie tried to grin through her discomfort. Frankly, the last thing she wanted was for any client to see her sweating through a vinyasa or losing balance in a tree pose.

"You can read me well. I guess Tanner knew what he was doing." Joe nodded. "I'm more of a weights-and-machines man. I'd be happy to spot you if you want to give it a try sometime." He leaned his arm on the table, tilted his head, and grinned at her.

Oh yeah, that earlier eye thing had been a wink. She needed to set some ground rules here. He obviously didn't realize a life coach was different from a friend.

"So, Joe, back to you."

He tilted his head toward her. "Enough about me, sweetheart."

Sweetheart?

"Tell me about you."

Sweetheart?

"Joe." She dug around in her purse until she found a business card for Davis Life Solutions. "Here's my card.

It has my website on it where you'll find my full bio. I'm certified, and I promise you my credentials are solid. I am a professional. So, please don't take this the wrong way, but—"

"Wait a minute." Joe crossed his arms.

"Yes?"

"You're a life coach?"

"Yes."

"And you're here to coach me now?"

"Of course. What did you think?"

"Well, when Tanner said there was a woman here that he wanted to introduce to me, I thought . . . " He shrugged and grinned again.

Cassie widened her eyes, realizing the confusion. "I'm so sorry. I'm sure you're a lovely man, but I think some signals were crossed. Tanner was hoping . . . " What was Tanner hoping for? Tanner was hoping she wouldn't be able to help Joe. Of course, he set the man up to have false expectations. He didn't want to lose. "Tanner and I were talking, and he thought perhaps I could help you figure out the next steps. That's one of the things I do best. I help people figure out where to go next in their careers, their lives."

Joe stood. "Lady, my next steps are none of your business." With that, he pushed out his chair and disappeared inside the café.

###

"Thank you for connecting me with Cassie Davis." Alice Bradshaw walked Tanner out to the reception area of Digital Access Solutions. "She has some amazing ideas. I'm looking forward to partnering with her."

"That's excellent news. I just saw her this morning, and she didn't say a word to me."

"Well, I spoke with her assistant this morning. She may not have known yet. Regardless, it's one more positive thing you've done for my company. Better be careful. You'll end up on my full-time payroll."

Tanner laughed as he opened the door to leave. "I'll be in touch when the next team-building training is complete and ready to roll out." He'd never find himself on someone else's payroll. There wasn't a chance anyone would take away his freedom like that. He couldn't imagine a traditional nine-to-five job, tied down to a desk and answering to someone else.

Of course, he wouldn't mind having someone to answer to at home, someone to spend his downtime with, to decompress with at the end of the day. His mind turned to Cassie, and he wondered what she did at the end of the day. Did she have plants? Pets? Was she more of a cat person or a dog person? He definitely would prefer a dog himself. What was going on with him? Tanner Clark didn't do settling down, commitments—pets! Just because the woman had pretty eyes, and hair, and a great smile, and was intelligent...

His cell rang as soon as he started his car.

"Thanks a lot!" Cassie's voice boomed through the speaker.

"You're welcome." Cassie must be super happy with him as Tanner sarcastically thinks to himself.

"I can't believe you did that."

"It was nothing. Just an introduction."

"Not quite an introduction."

"Semantics, whatever. It worked."

There was silence while he pulled out of the parking lot of DAS.

"Cassie? Did I lose you?" That was odd. He had all the cell signal bars on his phone.

"What are you talking about? Nothing has happened. Nothing worked."

"Well, not yet, of course. Do life coaches always expect instant results?"

"We only expect results when the client knows what's going on."

"Wait a second. I'm not even sure what's going on right now. Are you talking about Alice and DAS?"

"Tanner, I'm talking about Joe. It seems your cousin thought you were introducing him to me as an eligible bachelor. He thought it was a date."

The laughter exploded out of him at the idea of Joe—in his stained T-shirts, worn-out denim, and seahorse posture—dating Cassie. "A date? There's no way he thought that."

"What did you tell him?" she demanded.

He had to pull over to the side of the road so he could pick up his phone and listen to her. "I told him . . . " Well, he'd told him very little. Joe had informed him he was "not in a Tanner mood," so he'd kept it as short and sweet as possible. "Look. My cousin isn't always happy to see me."

"I can understand the feeling."

"I was a bit rushed when I spoke to him. I didn't want to make him any angrier. I can see now how he misinterpreted the situation, but I did not intend for him to think that. I swear."

She didn't respond. As the quiet seconds stretched out, Tanner realized he had been holding his breath and let out a gush of air right into the phone. Then he gulped audibly as he attempted to breathe normally again.

"Tanner?" She sounded concerned.

"I'm sorry. I didn't handle the introductions well. I see that now. I guess this means it didn't go so well?"

"To put it mildly. I know you want to win the bet, but I didn't expect you to set me up like that."

"It was not intentional, I promise. Joe never would have agreed to meet with you if I'd approached him and said, 'I know this life coach who wants to help you.'"

Cassie was quiet for so long that Tanner looked to see if perhaps they'd been disconnected.

"Cassie?"

"I'm here. I'm trying to figure out how to respond

to you. Because on one hand, I understand what you're saying. But why did you take me over there without any warning? We didn't have to go today. You could have spent a little time letting me know what I was up against. You could have explained things a bit more clearly to Joe, or at least made it clear I was not there to date him. He was greatly disappointed in the end and likely wants nothing to do with me now."

Was she giving up? He had been looking forward to spending the next few months watching her attempt to help Joe, and he was looking forward to getting to see her more often. But if she was ready to just buy him a cup of coffee, maybe he could turn it into a dinner date. Maybe he would still get to spend more time with her going forward, and it would have nothing to do with his cousin, Joe. Tanner got control of his thoughts. "Well, I know this great place on the lake that has amazing coffee—"

"Oh no. Not yet. I'm not giving up. I'm just getting my bearings."

He liked the confidence in her voice, but she ended the call before Tanner could even ask her about Alice Bradshaw.

CHAPTER 5

Regroup, Renew, Recommit

Cassie stormed into the Making Connections office and threw herself into the chair across from Micki.

"Oh no! The audition didn't go so well?" Micki looked up from her computer monitor. "I wondered why I hadn't heard anything from you. There will be other opportunities, Cass. You know that. Besides, we have bigger fish to batter."

"Fry." Cassie stared at the ceiling.

"What?"

"Fish to fry. The saying is 'we have bigger fish to fry.'"

"But you can't fry fish unless you batter them."

Cassie lifted her head to smile at Micki. "What else are we frying?"

"Alice Bradshaw called this morning."

Cassie gripped the arms of her chair. "And?"

"She wants to partner with Making Connections as a mentor—but that's not all."

"Can it get any better?"

"DAS is planning a massive expansion over the next couple of years. She said she's excited about the mentoring opportunity because then they can turn into 'future employees.' She was as excited about this as we are."

Cassie's grip couldn't keep her in her chair. She bounced out and began pacing. "That's amazing! Do you realize what this means? We have the support of the area's largest employer. This is going to be huge for us."

"See? We don't need that stupid TV spot."

"Oh." She stopped pacing. "I got the 'stupid' TV spot."

Micki frowned at Cassie. "I always assumed people were happy after an audition goes well and they land the gig. You were definitely not happy when you came in."

"Oh, that." Cassie returned to her chair. "That had nothing to do with the news audition . . . " Cassie stopped mid-sentence when realized how empty Micki's desk was. The usual stacks and folders and piles were missing, replaced by just one lonely little stack of papers. "Is the computer system up?"

"Up and running like a dream." Micki bounced her head, the pencil holding her mound of dark curls in place, wobbling precariously. "I'm entering all the information for people who have registered for services. There are four letters on your desk from companies that want to sponsor the career fair—with checks."

"Today is a *really* good day." Cassie pinched the bridge of her nose. She couldn't believe she'd let Tanner get under her skin like that. It was unlike her to become so overwhelmed by negative assumptions. Why was she letting Tanner shift her perspective like that? And Joe, why was she so angry he'd thought they were on a date? It was actually funny when she thought about it—a coaching client thinking they were dating. A giggle bubbled up inside her.

"What's so funny?" Micki asked.

Cassie filled her in on what had happened with Tanner, Joe, and the café.

"Wait. Joe Clark? Why do I know that name?" Micki turned in her chair to face her computer and began typing.

"He used to be in the restaurant business." Cassie looked at the monitor over Micki's shoulder. "I remember seeing his name in the news. Some kind of 'fall from grace' story."

"Right. Here it is." Micki's cursor traced the web results until she clicked on one. "Joseph Clark founder of Clark Enterprises files chapter eleven bankruptcy." She began reading silently to herself. "Wow, he made some really poor business decisions."

"Like what?" Cassie asked, returning to her seat.

"Well, he definitely seems to have had an ego. Apparently, just about every investor in the city wanted a piece of his business. He took it all in, whether he needed it or not, and, well, according to this, it's not clear where all the money went, but it doesn't seem to have gone into the restaurants. Some of them were eventually shut down for health code violations and—"

"Don't tell me which restaurants. I think I'd rather not know." Cassie shuddered.

"Apparently he'd been investing in his luxury life-style and not in his restaurants. When investors wanted to recoup their money, it was basically all gone, and the restaurants were too. Mr. Big Shot quickly became a Mr. Nobody."

"And now he's Mr. Janitor at a café."

"What are you going to do?"

"About what?"

"About Joe."

"I don't know that I can do much. You can't help someone if they don't want to be helped. And maybe this one is just beyond my reach. I mean, it doesn't sound like he has the capacity to turn things around if those were the choices he made."

Micki gaped at her friend, speechless.

"What?" Cassie asked.

"You have to help him. Everyone else gave up on him. You can't do that too. You have to help Joe." Micki pounded her fist against her desk as she spoke.

"But he doesn't want my help. He doesn't seem to want anybody's help. And with the new business devel-opments, I don't know. I'd much rather spend my time with people who want my input."

"Since when are you a quitter, Cassie?"

Ouch. Was she quitting?

Micki continued before Cassie could say anything else. "Do you remember the zucchini chips at Victory Heights?"

"With the parmesan crust? Oh, those were amazing. I miss that place."

"Joe was responsible for those, and everything else on that menu. We loved that place. You have the opportunity of a lifetime here." Micki slowly walked around her desk and grabbed Cassie by the shoulders. "You alone can get that man back in the kitchen. You alone can bring those zucchini chips back into our lives. You cannot turn down this mission."

###

"So, after yellow tulips, what do I send?" Tanner leaned over to sniff a lily. His nose tingled so strongly it twitched. He sneezed.

"Not those." Marley moved the lily pot away from him. "At least, not until I snip the pollen off. She's still upset with you?"

"Upset? That's a good question." He picked up a plant with small, glossy-green leaves. No flower in sight. Maybe that would be better. Something that could endure for years to come and that wouldn't make anyone sneeze. "I mean, I did something good for her, but I also accidentally set her up for an awkward situation."

"How awkward?" Marley filled a water canister.

"Well, she's a life coach, and I thought maybe she could help Joe."

"That's a great idea!" She poured the water into a large bowl with a chunk of florist foam set in the center.

"Don't congratulate me yet." He moved on to a row of miniature orchids. Beautiful, but somehow, sterile. No personality. "Joe misinterpreted me. He thought she was there to make a love connection."

Marley stopped what she was doing. "Please tell me you're joking."

"I wish I was." He picked up a bonsai, then immediately put it back. What was he doing, anyway? Was he just trying to tell Cassie he was sorry for the mix-up with Joe? Or was he trying to change the impression she had of him? Why did he care so much what she thought? She was popping into his head way too much.

"So, what happened?" Marley stared at him. He knew she'd continue staring until he said everything, so he started speaking. He filled her in on everything from the coffee in the café to the bet.

"Cassie Davis?" Marley shoved his shoulder hard enough for him to lose balance. What is it with women punching him in the shoulder? "Is this the same Cassie Davis from the workforce program with the city?"

"She used to be. She branched out on her own."

"She's amazing!"

"How do you know her?"

"She helped me get the help I needed for this store. In fact, that's why Dylan and I decided to have another baby. Without her, I'd still be working here around the clock. She saved us by helping me find reliable, good help to support me and the store. She does amazing work."

"I'm sure she does. She's amazing. But she doesn't like me much."

A grin spread across Marley's freckled face. "Oh, goodness."

"What?"

"I think somebody has a crush."

"I'm an adult. Adults don't get crushes, sister dear."

"Well, what do you call it then? Clearly you have feelings. Clearly—"

"Not another word, or I'm encouraging Joe to live in your basement forever."

"If you've got Cassie working with him, that won't matter. If anybody can get him turned around, it's her. I have complete faith in Cassie. He'll be out of there in time for us to redo the basement and the nursery. You, however . . . " She dragged him by his arm to the other side of the store. "You need a little help." She picked up a vase full of pink roses. "Take these to her. As in, you put them in your car and drive over to her office and deliver them in person. Call first to be sure she's there."

"Is that really necessary?"

"You're not just saying you're sorry for this mix-up. You're saying you're sorry, and you want to continue your relationship, right?"

"A relationship? I mean, we just met this week."

"Yes, and you're already sending her flowers. For a second time. Listen. I promise you won't break out in a rash just for thinking about things like relationships. A friendship is a relationship, after all. Why don't you start with that goal and see what happens?"

"And pink flowers work for that?"

"Those two dozen pink roses do. Just trust me. What do you have to lose?"

CHAPTER 6

SECOND CHANCES

Cassie put her hand on the metal push-plate of the café's glass front door and steadied herself. It wasn't butterflies in her stomach. It was an overall sense of being out of her league. Since becoming a life coach, she'd only worked with people who'd intentionally sought her services. They were people who knew they wanted a better life or more clarity as they transitioned into a new era. She'd never needed to sell her coaching services—or coaching services in general— to someone before.

Why couldn't Joe make things easy on everyone?

Because there's little growth in easy, she knew. This was going to be an excellent experience for her, too. She just had to do what she did best. She pushed the door open and entered the café. "How does Joe take his coffee?" Cassie asked Evan.

"Plain-black, dark-roast."

"Wonderful! I'd like to order two of those, please." They had coffee in common. That could be a starting point. "Does he eat any of the pastries or other sweets?" Cassie gestured toward the display case.

Evan's eyes shifted left, then right. He leaned over the counter and signaled Cassie to do the same. "He hates what we make here. If you want to get on his good side, go across the street and get him one of their white-choc-olate-chip, macadamia-nut cookies."

"Good to know." She glanced at her watch. According to Tanner, Joe should be going on break in about ten minutes. She had time. "I'll be right back."

Sneaking in contraband baked goods was definitely a new trick for Cassie, but sometimes a girl's got to do what a girl's got to do. Soon, she was sitting at a table near the back of the café, where she could hear Joe grumbling about everything wrong in the kitchen.

He sped through the dining area, apparently not seeing Cassie, or not wanting to admit to seeing her. She nearly ran to meet up with him at the counter.

"Your break is on me." She tapped his arm.

Joe shook her off his arm. "I can buy my own coffee."

"I'm sure you can. But I already bought you a cup, and . . . " she leaned closer and dropped her voice to a whisper, "I have a white-chocolate-chip, macadamia-nut cookie for you as well."

Joe stopped and looked at her. "What do you want?"

"Just a few minutes of your time."

His shoulders rose and dropped with a deep breath. He glanced at Evan, who was completely ignoring them both. "Okay. Fine. Where's this cookie?"

She led him back to her table and slid his cup of coffee to him.

"I was promised baked goods."

"And you'll get the cookie." Cassie nodded. "But first you hear me out."

"That cookie better not be stale."

Cassie broke off a tiny piece to give to him, praying it wasn't stale.

He savored the bite with eyes closed. "Do you know what makes a good cookie?"

"Sugar?"

"The right amount. A good cookie is like good wine. It's perfectly balanced—the sweet is balanced with the nuance of the particular flavors. Those folks across the street get it right. The bozos in this kitchen still have a way to go before anything they make is worth buying."

"Have you told them that?"

"I told them they make horrible cookies."

"That's not the same as telling them what makes for a good cookie or how it might help their business."

"They're not interested."

"How do you know?"

"They'd ask me if they wanted to do better."

Cassie sipped her coffee and gave him a lopsided grin. "You think they'd ask the man who's always scowling and growling about what they're doing wrong for advice?"

"Yes . . . " His face fell. "Maybe."

"I'm betting not." The cookie really did look good. She wished she'd bought two of them. "I mean, when someone I know is always crabby, the last thing I want is to engage with them. Typically, when people are freely sharing insulting, unwelcome advice, nobody seeks them out for more tips."

"I'm not insulting." Joe leaned back in his chair and crossed his arms.

"Really?" She clicked on the note app on her phone. "While I waited for you, I couldn't help but hear you in the back. Here are a few phrases I caught: 'Apparently, no one has ever heard of a basting brush around here.'"

"He was using a spoon." Joe sniffed his coffee before sipping.

"I also heard a very clear, 'What a stupid idea!' I couldn't hear what you were talking about for that one. But then I heard, 'That's the dumbest way to store cheese.'" Cassie set her phone on the table. "So, what's the best way to store cheese?"

"It depends on the cheese. Cheese is a living thing. It needs to be cared for."

"Okay, that kind of scares me."

He spoke over her. "It should never be wrapped tightly in plastic. It needs to be able to sweat and breathe."

Cassie wasn't sure how she felt about sweaty cheese, but Joe's face was the calmest and most pleasant she'd ever seen it, so she let him continue.

"Plastic can suffocate cheese, which will make it taste as if it's been in an ammonia bath. Cheese, like that pecorino in the back, should be wrapped in wax paper—there is a specific paper for cheese—and then stored in a place where it will get adequate humidity. In commercial refrigerators, that generally means in a sealable bowl lined with a damp towel."

"Interesting." Joe knew about food and was obviously still in touch with his abilities in the kitchen. She would start there and build off his strengths. But first, she had to get him to agree to being coached. "So, next I heard you say . . . "

Joe stood up. "I'll buy my own cookie, thank you. I don't need to be abused."

"Wait!" Cassie stood, too, and reached for his arm. "I'll stop. I will. I wasn't trying to make you feel bad."

"Really? Because you were doing an excellent job."

"I was just trying to show you why people may be hesitant to ask for your help. If instead of telling someone what they are doing wrong, think of it as educating about the right way to do things. Just like you did just now with me. I've only been talking to you a few minutes, and I already learned so many things I didn't know before."

He returned to his seat and held out his hand. "My cookie?"

She broke the remaining part in half and handed him one portion.

"Do you know why Tanner asked me to speak to you?"

"I'm guessing," he said after he swallowed a bite,

"because he's a busybody who thinks he knows best and wants to tell everyone else how they should live."

Cassie realized there may be some truth to that; Tanner did seem pretty confident he had the right answers. "I think that's a valid point from someone in your position. And, perhaps, that's part of it. However, if you think all the way through that thought, it also becomes clear that he cares about you—a lot. He wants you to live your best life." Which she was sure he did. He wouldn't be the go-to guru for instilling positive energy into corporate culture or team building if he wasn't so passionate about wanting everybody to live that way.

"Who says I'm not living my best life right now?"

Cassie cocked her head to the side and gestured toward the coffee shop, Joe's dirty clothes, and the half a cookie she still hadn't given him. "Are you?"

"This is just interim." Joe's cheeks slightly reddened as he looked away.

"How long does this 'interim' last?"

He wiped the crumbs from the table into his palm, then dumped them on his napkin.

"What's the plan for shifting out of interim? What does post-interim look like for you?" She knew she was pushing him, and the comment could make him get up and leave, but she also knew that pushing people some-times worked.

He stood again. "I think I'm done here. Break time's over. Thanks for the cookie."

"Okay, Joe." Cassie stood, too. "But I'll be back again tomorrow. And the day after that. I'm fine coming here every day and asking those same questions until you give me an answer."

He took a step, then turned toward her. "Who are you again?"

"Cassie Davis. I'm a . . . " She realized that leading with her coaching was not going to win him over. "I wear a few hats. I run a nonprofit that matches mentees with career mentors."

He snorted. "You think I need to be mentored?"

Cassie tried not to let her grin get too wide. She had thrown out the bait and he bit without even looking to see if a line was attached. "Of course not. You know what you're doing in the kitchen. You'd make an excellent mentor. But how can I assign a mentee to you right now in your current position and frame of mind?"

He remained quiet for a while, sucking on his cheeks. She applauded his comfort level in taking his time to answer questions.

"So, I am also a life coach."

He rolled his eyes. "I had one of those before. She loved herself a lot."

"I'm different. Career transitions are what I specialize in. I help people figure out what their next move should be and how to make it happen. I'm just taking a guess here, but I don't think you want to be a restaurateur again, do you?"

"I do not."

"And I'm guessing you don't want to be a cranky janitor for the rest of your life."

"There's nothing wrong with being a janitor."

"Of course there isn't. But you are miserable in this job, and there's nothing right about that."

"I wouldn't say I'm miserable."

"Joe, you became a different person when you started teaching me about cheese storage. Your whole body relaxed, and your tone of voice shifted. You're meant to be in the food industry, maybe just not the part of the industry that does all the cleanup."

"I don't want to be a restaurateur again."

"I'm not saying you should. There are plenty of other jobs in the food world."

"I don't want to cook or be a chef. They work weekends and holidays."

"So, you want a social life. I get it." She picked up her to-go cup. "That's a start. How about we make a deal? I help you figure out what your next career move is, and you agree that when you're ready, you take on a mentee from my program."

"Why are you doing this?"

"Well, Tanner and I . . . " She caught herself before discussing the bet. The bet with Tanner suddenly felt awful and ill-conceived. Placing a bet on someone else's life, their livelihood, that wasn't how she worked. Helping people thrive in their careers was her *why*. How had she lost sight of that? "Tanner told me about you, and I think I can help. This is what I do. It's what gives me purpose and I enjoy it."

"Really?" He narrowed his eyes and she could imagine the thoughts racing through his mind.

"Really. And your zucchini chips."

"My what?" he asked, confused for a moment. Then, she could see the realization settling in.

"You need to make sure those are back in the world."

CHAPTER 7

FACING TRUTHS

The pink roses were definitely past their prime. Wilted and drooping, they collapsed in on themselves a little. "I can't give these to her now, can I?" Tanner asked Marley.

"No!" Marley took the vase from him. "I put this together a week ago. What have you done with them?"

"I thought that was apparent: nothing."

"Why didn't you give them to her?"

"I'm not sure." He jumped up on the counter and sat, watching his sister take apart the once-beautiful arrangement.

Marley raised an eyebrow and stared him down. "Care to at least take a guess?"

"There just didn't seem to be a reason to." He couldn't meet her eyes.

"Don't ever play poker."

"You're not the first to tell me that." He tilted his head back, but the laugh was fake, forced. Suddenly, he didn't want to talk about Cassie.

"Because your face never lies." Marley touched his arm, and the gentleness in her voice lodged an unsettled feeling in his stomach.

He shook off her hand, jumped down from the

counter, and rounded on her. "I guess I just didn't feel like giving her flowers. It felt silly."

"I get it. Tanner Clark, perennial bachelor, the man who can commit to nothing, found himself scared of feelings for someone. It makes sense."

"I'm not scared." This wasn't the kind of verbal sparring he expected from his sister. This felt too . . . real. "Just because you dove headfirst into marrying someone and starting a family as soon as you could, doesn't mean everyone else wants that."

His words surprised him. He'd never said anything like that to his sister before, but it seemed so obvious now. Not long after their parents had died in a car accident, Marley was suddenly fixated on moving out and starting a new family. It had been all she talked about. Of course, she'd been trying to fill the void their parents' deaths had created.

Maybe that was what she'd needed. But she'd also just assumed that was what he needed too, and that wasn't fair. As far back as he could remember, she'd been trying to shove him into a relationship with someone—anyone. But that was Marley's path in life, not his.

She dumped the old flowers in a refuse bin. "You sound a little defensive to me."

"I'm not. Look, I enjoy being a free agent. I like my freedom." He rounded the counter to kiss his sister on the cheek. "I'm sorry I didn't take better care of the flowers.

That was a poor decision on my part. But at least now you don't need to replace them. And I don't think I'll be bothering you for more plants or flowers for Cassie any time soon."

"Tanner." Marley caught his arm and held him in place.

He took advantage of a sudden chime on his phone to shake free from her. "This might be a client." He pulled the phone out of his pocket and stepped away from his sister. It wasn't a client. It was Joe.

At least she didn't give me a bumper sticker.

Genuine laughter erupted from him. "I guess Joe has a new life coach after all," he said to Marley, showing her the text.

"What does he mean about a bumper sticker, though?" Marley studied the message.

"Gabi Gold tried to work with Joe before. It didn't pan out. Do you know who she is?"

"Enormous hair, loud voice, calls everyone 'sweetheart?'"

"That's her."

"Seriously, Tanner? No wonder the man is still on my couch!"

"Gabi rewarded him for being so attentive during their first meeting by giving him a bumper sticker."

"But Joe doesn't have a car. He rides a bike."

"That made it even worse." Tanner laughed, clutching

his stomach. "And the bumper sticker said, 'Be fantastic, just like me!'"

"Oh, good grief. That's awful." Marley was close enough to grab Tanner's arm again, and this time she wasn't letting him slip away from her. "Listen, Tanner. I get your whole 'free agent' schtick. I do. Losing Mom and Dad was hard on all of us. Letting people in can't be easy for you, but that doesn't mean it's not worth it."

"Marley, you're not a good armchair psychologist. It's not a schtick. I've let plenty of people in. I have you. I have Gram. Maybe that's all I need."

"You're stuck with Gram and me, and you hold on tight to us. But that can't be all you need." She released his arm.

When he said nothing in return, she asked, "Who's your closest friend?"

Tanner blinked a few times. "I have friends."

"Close friends?"

"You and I are close," he responded, realizing that he couldn't imagine sharing as much of himself with anyone else like he did his sister. But that didn't mean it was a problem, did it?

"What about someone who isn't your sister?" She pursed her lips and watched as the wheels in his mind began turning.

He could let people in when he wanted to. Couldn't he?

###

Taping her first Monday Motivation Minute was anticlimactic for Cassie. She had envisioned sitting at the anchor desk, bantering with the other members of the newscast. But they had placed her in a private studio and had her read her message—in four takes because she wasn't "amped" enough for the first three—and sent her on her way. Didn't they realize how hard it was to be "amped" as she spoke to a tiny image of herself beaming from a little monitor connected to a camera?

It had been nothing like her audition. But now she knew what to expect and vowed to be better prepared for the next time. She left the station and headed toward the café, realizing that being alone in a closet-like space was an opportunity to practice what she preached to clients. When a situation turns out different from what you expect, you focus on how you handle it. Disappointment doesn't have to lead to reluctance. It can be seen as an opportunity. It was all about perspective. All she had to do was focus on reaching a point where she was excited and joyously expectant of something good coming from the segment—even if recorded in a closet. Positive outcomes can come from the most unexpected places if you let them.

She headed straight toward the café, confident and secure that all was right in the world. Though she had thought she might see Tanner at the station again. She quickly pushed that thought away and took a detour to pop into a bakery for a pumpkin-spiced muffin. Then, she bought two white-chocolate-chip, macadamia-nut cookies from the bakery across from the coffee shop before heading in to order two plain-black, dark-roast coffees.

But Joe wasn't working that day.

"What do you mean, 'he's not here?'" she asked Evan.

"He's not scheduled to work today."

Cassie looked at the calendar on her phone. She had set this appointment with Joe. She tapped a finger to her chin. Not a problem, she decided. She'd just show up where he lived, and bring the muffin, cookies, and coffee. "Okay, I'll take those to go."

"They're in the same kind of cup." Even shrugged. "You okay with that?"

"I don't care one way or another." And she meant it. She tapped into her contacts and scrolled to Tanner's name. To find Joe, she needed to get his sister's address. She clicked on Tanner's name, but suddenly her fingers wouldn't do anything else. They hovered over the screen of her phone. She hadn't seen Tanner in over a week. Hadn't even heard from him since she'd won Joe over. She'd thought about calling or texting Tanner over the past couple of days, but every time she almost did, she talked herself out of it. They weren't friends. Just acquaintances with a bet. They didn't really have a reason to talk to each other, did they?

"Sorry I'm late." Joe whizzed by. "Meet me in the kitchen when you're ready."

Cassie startled and looked around. "Did Joe just zoom through here?" she asked Evan.

"Either that or a lightning bolt struck." He placed the two coffees on a tray. "Listen, Donna will be here today. She only tolerates Joe because no one has answered her 'help wanted' ad to replace him." He passed the tray to her. "Tanner brought you here, so in my book, whatever you want with Joe must be a good thing. But that other woman Tanner introduced to him was a loud, self-promoting mess. Our customers don't come here to have a total stranger sit at their table and tell them to smile a little so their problems won't be a big deal. Donna was happy to kick her out."

"That must have been Gabi."

Evan nodded.

"No worries!" She loaded the cookies and muffins on the tray. "I won't bother anyone but Joe."

She found him sitting on a stack of empty crates near the back door in the kitchen. "Good morning, Joe." Glancing around, it was clear there was no place for her to sit. "I was hoping we could relax at a table in the dining room." She set the tray on a long counter.

"Nah. I want to stay right here." He nodded to the large garbage can next to him.

"Any particular reason?"

"This gives me the best view of everything going on in this kitchen." He looked beyond her. "I can keep my eye out for everything they're doing wrong back here. I want to use my time productively. See, you didn't even need to coach me on productivity."

Cassie twisted around and noticed for the first time the two staff members milling about on the other side of the kitchen. They turned their backs toward Joe and Cassie, and she got the distinct feeling they were being ignored.

"I'm not here to help you improve your time management." She turned to Joe again. "I'm here to help you kick start a new era in your life." She raised the tray. "I have coffee and cookies. I'll be out in the dining room. Regardless of how long you stay in here, I'll start our hour together the minute you arrive out there."

It didn't take long before Joe found his way out to the dining room where Cassie and the coffee and cookies were.

"You must not have many clients." He sat opposite her at the same table they'd used before.

"Why do you say that?" She handed him a coffee and a cookie, then spread out the paper holder from her muffin to use it as a make-shift plate.

"I could have made you sit here all day."

"Well, that would have been inconvenient. But I intentionally have a light coaching load right now because I'm focused on my nonprofit. After our meeting this morning, I'll be meeting with my partner, Micki, for the rest of the day at our office to strategize mentoring connections and create the curriculum for a couple of classes we'll be teaching to job seekers. Micki knows what I'm doing here. She'll understand if I need more time."

"Why couldn't we meet at your office?"

"Well," she sipped her coffee. "The office is new for us. We just moved in. The building used to be a preschool, so it has nice classrooms, suitable office space, and even a commercial kitchen. However," she leaned back in her chair, "our grant only covered the building. And until we can afford new furniture, meetings there have to happen at a table built for someone less than half an adult's size." She grinned as she imagined Joe hunched over a tiny table.

"How do you expect to buy new furniture?"

"We have plenty of fundraising activities planned. One of which is a career fair where companies sponsor . . . " She realized then what Joe was doing. If he got her talking enough about her work, they'd have little time left to talk about him. "None of that matters, Joe. We don't need to distract ourselves from why we're both really here."

He shrugged.

"Let's get started." She pulled a three-ring binder and

a few pens from her attaché. Joe could certainly work a room if he wanted. That gruff demeanor must all be for show. "I think you made a wise move when you chose to work in this café."

"Will you inform the rest of my family?"

"People tell themselves they work at a job for numerous reasons. They need or want the income or benefits is often the primary one. However, ultimately, at the root of the decision to work anywhere is the concept of movement. You are either moving toward something—a better life, career expansion, some kind of goal—or you are moving away from something; running away from responsibilities, stress, overload."

Joe grunted.

"My guess is the latter for you. You came here instead of going back to where you were—"

"You make it sound like I had a choice. No one would back me to start a new restaurant."

"You didn't give anyone a chance, though, did you?"

He bit into his cookie and chewed slowly.

"Which means, that's not what you really wanted."

He continued chewing. Cassie assumed that meant she was right. "Let's talk a little today about what you didn't like when you had your company. Let's try to figure out what you were moving away from when you came here."

"What's the point?"

"Knowing what you don't want is a perfect bounce point. Getting clear on that will help you figure out where you want to go, so when you make the rebound, you can head in the direction of what you want."

"You make rebounding sound easy. But have you ever actually done it?"

Ouch. It was Cassie's turn to take a bite and chew. The pumpkin spice muffin was delicious, but the sweetness of it couldn't erase the sour memories. Should she tell Joe? Would that help him believe in himself? "I have. And, in some respects, you could say I'm still on my way up from the bounce."

"What happened?"

"I used to be in charge of the city's workforce development department." She sipped her coffee.

"And?"

"And they fired me." That was the first time she didn't use the words let go, which was somehow, cathartic. She'd expected to feel vulnerable, but admitting the truth wound up empowering her. "I was a bit overenthusiastic, according to the city. They wanted to rein in some of the programs, and I wanted to expand. They wanted me to streamline our processes, and I wanted to create systems we could tailor to each individual who came to us."

"And they fired you because of a difference of opinion?"

"They fired me because I thought I'd prove them wrong and do things my way, anyway. Only I didn't think about my budget and the resources available to me. I wound up unable to meet any of the goals the city set for me, and instead, I ended up with an assortment of disconnected programs and services that were under-staffed and under-equipped."

Joe nodded. "I can see why they canned you. That's no way to run a business."

"I see it now, too. But I learn from my mistakes." She cheered him with her cup and took a sip. "Which is what I want to help you do. Getting fired was the best thing that could have happened to me. It made me take the time to truly figure out what I wanted to do and how I would go about doing it."

"Lucky me. I got a role model in failure."

CHAPTER 8

RISKY BUSINESS

Tanner double-checked the address on Cassie's business card. Yes, this bright, yellow building with the giant A-B-C blocks outside was the right place. Did she work in a preschool, too? A life coach, a mentoring nonprofit, and a preschool? Oh, and the Monday morning spot on the news as well. Clearly, the woman needed to set some boundaries. How could she expect to succeed at everything if she spread herself so thin?

He stepped out of his car. There were only two others in the lot. How does a preschool survive with only two teachers? He stood, holding the new bouquet Marley had made in both hands like a basketball. He was tempted to get back in his car and drive away. But what if she had already seen him standing there? Besides, even if she was a flighty life coach, a nonprofit CEO, and a preschool teacher, he still liked the idea of seeing her. He hadn't even talked to her in weeks, and yet she still kept popping into his mind. He was drawn to her, and Marley was right: what harm could a little bouquet do? He was trying to build a friendship.

Though the bouquet he carried was definitely not little. Marley had put together two dozen pink roses, interspersed with several white hydrangeas. It was gorgeous and probably weighed ten pounds. Being inconspicuous now was out of the question. He was going in.

"Can I help you?" A woman with a massive amount of black curly hair piled on her head was sitting behind a desk, completely covered in papers and files.

"Um, is Cassie here? Does Cassie Davis work here?" The place was a disaster. There were manila files and accordion folders covering every possible surface. But no sounds of children. What kind of school was this?

"She's in her office. I can sign for the flowers." The woman wasn't even looking at him. She was shuffling through the mess on her desk.

"I'd rather give them to her myself."

That got the woman's attention. She stopped, looked him up and down—twice—and frowned. "You're not with a delivery company?"

"No."

"Who are you?" She folded her arms across her chest.

"Hey, Micki, have you seen the clipboard with . . . "

Cassie entered the reception area carrying even more paper. She stopped when she saw him. "Tanner! What are you doing here?"

"You know him? He doesn't have an appointment and—"

"It's okay, Mick." Cassie tapped the ends of the paper on Micki's desk to align them. "This is the gentleman who introduced me to Alice Bradshaw. Micki, meet

Tanner Clark. Tanner, this is Micki Holmes. She's my partner in crime here."

The place was such a mess, Tanner wanted to turn around and leave. But Cassie looked so pretty in her emerald-green sweater. The flowers were a leaden weight in his arms. "These are for you." He held them out.

"More flowers!" Cassie handed the papers to Micki to accept the vase. Her arms visibly dropped; the weight must have surprised her. "They're beautiful."

"Oh . . . my sister runs a flower shop." *What? Why did he say that?*

"Oh. Well, I love fresh flowers. Thank you, again." Her smile melted his core. "So, um . . . "

He was suddenly aware of having nothing to say. He had been so focused on just wanting to see her again that his planning had not gone any farther than that.

"Well, thank you, Mr. Clark," Micki interrupted his thoughts. "But I think we owe you flowers. We're so excited to have DAS as a partner. It's not official yet, but Cassie is meeting with them in a couple of days. It's going to be a beautiful alliance."

"That's excellent news." Tanner found his voice.

Micki stood and pushed back her chair. She opened her arms wide, gesturing to the avalanche of paper and mess surrounding her. "Obviously, we could probably use DAS on a couple of fronts. Excuse the mess in here. Our computer system is a bit temperamental."

"That's an understatement," Cassie added.

"So, Cassie," Micki opened her eyes wide as she looked at her. "Why don't you give Mr. Clark a tour? There are plenty of spots of the building not quite as overwhelmed as my work space out here."

"Great idea. Let me put the flowers in my office, and I'll show you around."

Tanner followed her to a small, tidy office and breathed a sigh of relief.

"We've only been here a couple of weeks, so we have had very little time to actually change anything. Nor do we have the funds. The career fair should help, though." She set the flowers on her desk. "These are really lovely."

Those eyes again! What could he say? "I was in my sister's shop and, well, I wanted to come see you. I didn't want to come empty-handed."

"You'd be welcome without the flowers."

His heart skipped, and his stomach churned. Did he have heartburn?

"Well," she headed back toward the door to her office, "let me show you around and give you some insight on us before you speak at the career fair."

"Oh!" He'd forgotten he'd said he'd speak at the fair. "Yes. Tell me all about the work you're doing."

She led him through the building, explaining how she planned to use the money from the career fair to turn the pre-K classes into adult-oriented rooms for skills training. "Though, frankly, the way our luck's been running with computers around here, I'm a little afraid to offer people office skills training that includes things like Word and Excel."

"You're having problems?"

"You didn't notice the fire trap on Micki's desk? It's a brand-new system, but for some reason, it just shuts down on us, and everything gets wiped out."

"Do you have—"

"Cloud backup? Yes." They'd returned to her office. "Which is great for when we get up and running again. Everything is still there, but we have so much information coming in all the time. Micki prints it from her home computer and brings it in here to organize. It's all dossiers on people and companies that we need to match together for job training. It's exciting to have so much interest, but we're barely able to keep up, even when our computer system works properly."

"Is there anything I can do to help?"

"You are doing something. You're speaking at our career fair. If I could print anything, I'd give you some flyers. I'd love to put your name and whatever logo you have on them. And add it to our Facebook event. You have my card, right?"

"I do." He had it, but now it felt like him having her card was more important to him than it was to her. Clearly, she was more interested in him for business than anything personal. Maybe Marley was right: maybe he didn't want to risk an actual connection with anyone or anything. The disappointment he was feeling right now, over a business card, was more than enough.

Tanner left so quickly, Cassie wasn't sure if she'd entered a time warp. One minute they were pleasantly talking about the career fair and the next, boom! It was as if a starting gun had sounded and he was out the door. He just said goodbye and sped away. The man was definitely not good at departures. Although, as she stood at the front window and watched him get in his car and leave, she worried that maybe he wasn't the awkward one. Had she misread signals?

She joined Micki in one of the classrooms and scrunched herself in a child-sized chair at a child-sized table. "Why do you think he brought flowers?"

"Don't be dense, Cass." Micki had spread papers in two orderly rows lining both sides of the table. "He's interested in you. Not the nonprofit."

"Then why hasn't he said so?"

"Maybe you're not giving him a chance." Micki took the chair opposite her. "We're going to need to partner with a chiropractor if we don't manage to get new furniture soon. This is getting to be ridiculous."

"Agreed. Let's do this quickly." They were using the table as a makeshift floor plan of the high school gym where they'd be holding the career fair. The papers represented the various vendors who'd paid to have a company booth. The strategy was to ensure no competing companies were next to each other and that the primary sponsors—Alice Bradshaw of DAS and a local health care firm—had the best visibility.

"It's almost overwhelming how many businesses are interested in this," Cassie said. "Do we have any idea how many people are going to attend?"

"If you think this is overwhelming, don't look at the Facebook event page." Micki helped Cassie pile the papers in a neat stack, in numbered order so they'd remember which vendor would be placed where at the fair. "If half the people who expressed interest in coming attend, then each of these vendors will have about a hundred separate people visiting their tables."

"Not that many will come, though." Cassie both equally hoped that what she said was right and dreaded she was wrong. "Do you think we should find a food vendor?"

"Maybe at least someone for coffee, water, and pastries."

"I had the best pumpkin muffin the other day. Maybe I'll approach them."

"Why not the coffee place where Joe works?"

"We don't want to scare away the participants."

Micki tilted her head. "Joe's food is fantastic."

"He's the janitor, not the cook, remember? I don't think he wants to cook. I think he's more interested in telling the cooks what to do."

"Does he want to instruct?"

"Maybe. We haven't got there yet. I still don't know what he wants to do." She leaned back as best she could in the diminutive chair as Micki placed another stack of paper in front of her. "I guess it's time to play the mentor match game, huh?"

"Mentor match! Why didn't we think of that for a company name?"

"Too late now." Cassie laughed. "Besides, it doesn't include everything else we're doing here. The classes, the coaching, the—oh no, Micki." Her giggles subsided as a dawning realization took hold.

"What's up?"

"Am I doing it again?"

"Doing what?"

"The mentor matching, the career fair, the TV thing, the coaching. Is it too much? Am I spreading myself too thin? Are they all going to fail because I'm just adding on and not making room for it all?"

Micki pulled a pencil out of her hair, letting it tumble down to her shoulders. She shook her head, her curls flying loose. "To be honest, Cass, I've been worried about that. But I've been watching your calendar, and you have really cut back on coaching clients. If we can just find a couple more people to help with the classes, so much won't have to be on your shoulders."

"We're in the running for that adult education grant, which would help us pay instructors for the classes, especially the leadership courses. Until we find out about the grant, maybe we could find some volunteer instructors. People in the community who would be willing to lend us some of their time."

"Like . . . Mr. Flowers?"

"Who?"

Micki cocked her head and waited.

Cassie smiled. "Tanner would be good at it."

"And you'd get to spend time with him —professionally."

"You say that like it's a bad thing."

"Because that's not what you want, and judging by the size of that bouquet, that's not what he wants, either."

"I can't find the time for anything more."

"Wait a minute. Isn't that one of your coaching phrases? You don't find time, you make it."

CHAPTER 9

CLEAN LIVING

"How do you live like this?" Tanner was almost afraid to remove a towel from the armchair in Marley's basement, but he did, pinching it between his thumb and forefinger as if he were holding a spider by the leg. Thankfully, no spiders or any other critters climbed from under it—but what to do with it now?

"Easily." Joe snatched the towel, wadded it up into a ball, and tossed it toward a hamper. "Two points!" he hollered when it went in. "I rarely have visitors. What's the point in cleaning?" He flopped on the sofa.

"But *you're* here. Doesn't it bother you?"

Joe glanced around the room. "Only when I think about it, which I try to do as little as possible."

"Right." Tanner nodded. Cleaning up meant paying attention to his situation, taking responsibility for what he's done. When would Joe grow up?

"So, what brings you to my humble basement?" Joe plopped his feet on the coffee table.

"To remind you, it's not yours." Tanner knew how harsh his voice was, but someone needed to get Joe's attention. "You do realize Marley—"

"Wants me out soon? She's expecting another kid in April. I'm aware. In fact, I've spoken to Dylan and told him not only will I be out in March, but I'll help him paint and do whatever needs to be done down here."

Tanner relaxed in his chair. Why hadn't Marley mentioned that? "That sounds like great news. But March is a lot different from the 'couple weeks' you said—a couple of weeks ago."

"Yeah. Well, something came up."

"This is why . . . " none of us trusts you, Tanner almost said. Instead, he took a different route. "Joe, you have to level with yourself, even if you won't level with me. These excuses have to stop"

"Wow. I didn't realize you liked to kick a dog when it's already down, Tanner."

"I'm not kicking. I'm just worried."

"I'll ignore that patronizing tone in your voice." Joe reached under the sofa and pulled out a laptop computer. "Let me show you something."

Since when did he have a laptop? It was a nice one, too.

Joe shoved a sock and pillow off the sofa and patted the empty space. "Come over here."

Tanner wished he had a spray disinfectant handy. But he sat next to his cousin, anyway.

Joe opened the computer and clicked into a program. "Look." He pointed to a row of numbers in a spreadsheet.

"These are the amounts I've been able to tuck away every week."

"Okay." It wasn't entirely clear to Tanner what he was looking at.

"Do you know how a chapter eleven works?" Joe clicked open a web browser.

"Not really."

"Good for you." Joe's voice didn't sound as sarcastic as Tanner would have expected. "It's actually an excellent program that's meant to protect everybody—the people owed money and the bozos who owe it."

Tanner watched as Joe logged into a bank account.

"I've been able to pay back just about every single person and investment group that backed me so far. I sold off all the property and most everything that was on it." He clicked on a link to a savings account with a pretty sizable sum of money. "I just need a little more in here, and I'll be able to pay off the last person . . . Gram."

"Gram gave you money?"

"Yeah, and seriously, every time I get close to paying her back, something happens."

"Like cat-scratch fever?"

"Who knew that was a thing, right?"

"That was real?"

"Yeah. I've been feeding the strays behind the café. I picked up the bowl once when I thought the last cat was done, but apparently, she was just taking a break. She pounced. My forearm swelled to twice its normal size."

Tanner laughed at the thought. Joe was so out of shape these days; it was hard to picture him with giant arms.

"I went to an urgent care clinic, and they cautioned me of the risks of cat-scratch fever. It's actually really dangerous."

Tanner attempted to rein in his laughter. "I'm actually relieved. I thought it was a pretty crappy excuse."

"Gram says she doesn't want the money back. She just wants me to be happy and to do something good with my life."

"That's what we all want."

Joe closed the laptop and picked up a three-ring-binder from the coffee table. "This came from Cassie. I have homework every week. I skimmed through to future weeks. She's really intent on getting to a person's core motivation, finding whatever they're passionate about so they can create a career around that."

Tanner was surprised, but he held back from admitting it. "That makes sense."

"This question got me." Joe leafed through until he found a page he'd dog-eared. "'Beyond your career, what's important for you in your life?' That's my next assignment. I'm supposed to think on that and come up with an answer."

Tanner realized Cassie was doing what Tanner had been trying to do all along. She was making Joe look hard at his life and figure out what motivates him.

Joe slammed the book shut. He stood and paced the room, taking giant steps around a few piles of laundry. "I realized what I want is to leave a positive legacy. I know I'm a long way away from that. And so far, I've left nothing but a trail of IOUs. But I want to support someone doing good in this world."

"That's awesome, Joe. What is your plan?"

"I'm not talking about my career decisions until I work them all out. I've had plenty of experience seeing disappointment on everyone's face. I'm not risking that again."

"Joe, nobody's judging you."

Joe gave him a side-eye before continuing. "Anyway, I need to take a course."

"What?"

"I need money to pay for courses to become certified."

"What kind of certification?"

"That's between Cassie and me. It's none of your business."

Tanner felt anxiety creep into his belly. Not because Joe didn't want to tell him what he was planning. But because now there seemed to be something between Joe and Cassie—something more than would ever be between Tanner and Cassie.

Alice Bradshaw was an amazing person. She blew Cassie away with her intuitiveness and humility. Cassie left their meeting feeling inspired with a renewed sense of confidence. Anything was possible, and she could see the height of success on the horizon.

She stopped in the café to see Joe. She'd seen him the day before, but they hadn't had time to discuss his homework.

Evan didn't take her order, Donna did.

"You've been in here before to talk to Joe," the café owner said. "You look like you have your life together. What on earth could you want with him?"

"Excuse me?" Cassie was confused by the question.

"You and Joe don't seem to be a match to me."

Cassie laughed as she accepted her coffee. "I'm his . . . " she remembered Evan's warning and how Donna was definitely not a fan of Gabi's. "He's teaching me about the restaurant business."

"If you want to learn, I'd be happy to hire you." Donna tapped on her register screen.

"No, thank you." Cassie handed her a credit card. "Let me clarify. I'm getting to know Joe. I have a nonprofit where people who are transitioning in careers can learn business skills and be mentored by others in new fields to them."

"Really?" Donna seemed genuinely interested. "What is Joe wanting to learn to do?"

"We're still working on that. But I was hoping I could get him to mentor people who want to go into the restaurant business."

"Really? That might be something I'd be interested in—"

"You here again, Cassie?" Joe interrupted, appearing from the back of the shop.

"Just checking to see how the homework is going, Joe." Cassie beamed him her best smile as she turned away from Donna.

"It's going." He pushed a bucket with a mop in it to the side of the ordering area and began cleaning the already spotless floor.

"Have you thought about your answers?" Cassie left her cup on the countertop and pulled three index cards from her pocket and read from the first. "I'd asked you to think on and answer these three questions. Number one: what are you passionate about?"

Joe put his mop in the bucket, twisted his mouth to one side, and sighed. "Things being done the right way."

She scribbled his answer on that card. "What skills do you have that you like to use?"

"Do we seriously have to do this where everybody and their uncle can hear me?"

Cassie looked around. Only she and Joe were in the

café's customer area. Donna stood on the other side of the ordering counter, staring at them.

"Would you prefer to write them down for yourself?"

"I'd prefer you just trust me to answer them and never bring this up again."

"I don't work that way."

"You'll just have to trust me and the process. I know what works." He mumbled so low, Cassie wasn't sure she heard correctly. She wrote it down anyway, knowing she'd be giving him a chance to clarify next week.

"Okay then, the last one: what do people in the world need?"

The corners of his mouth turned down as he looked at her under half-closed eyes. "What do other people in the world need? Do you seriously expect me to answer this?"

"I do. With total honesty to yourself and to me."

"It's a stupid question."

"You can think that, but you should still answer it. It'll provide insight into the kind of job you will thrive in."

"I thrived already." Joe turned his back on her. He pulled out his mop, put it through the bucket's wringer, and resumed mopping.

"Thriving isn't a one-time thing." Cassie carefully stepped over the puddle of water he'd created. "In fact, human beings are supposed to thrive. That's how innovation and creativity are able to continuously expand us to—"

"Do you know who the oldest Cassie on record is?" Joe faced her with such abruptness, she almost stumbled.

"What?" Cassie's mind raced as she tried to figure out what Joe was up to.

"Cassandra was a priestess in ancient Greece. She's in *The Iliad,* an old story, where she appears to be able to foretell the future, but no one takes her seriously. They don't listen to her."

Joe stared into Cassie's eyes. She knew he was trying to tell her something, but what was it? She waited.

"You're out there willing to connect Donna with a mentee. But she's not the right person. You need to read the future better. Donna will fail your mentee. Do you really think she has the chops to manage a place?"

"I really don't know. But this place seems to be doing well."

"This place is barely staying afloat. Connect your precious 'mentees,'" he made air quotes with his fingers, "with people who know what they're doing."

"Like who?"

Joe resumed mopping, didn't answer her.

"Joe?"

He continued mopping. "Been there, done that."

"So, do it again."

"Look. I did this stupid homework a couple of days

ago. I figured out what I want to do, what fired me up, what people need that I could offer. I was so excited about it. I couldn't wait to tell you."

"Awesome!"

"Not awesome. I cleaned my place and went to bed feeling like anything was possible last night. But you know who I saw in the mirror this morning?"

She didn't know how to answer that question.

"Me. I saw me. The guy who couldn't handle success. The man who failed so spectacularly that . . . " he looked up at the ceiling. "I can't risk doing that again."

"Oh, Joe," Cassie reached a hand out to him.

A loud crash and the sound of glass breaking sounded from the back dining area. A small child began to cry.

"Now there's someone who needs me. Some kid threw their breakfast on the floor—that's what I do now." Joe took his mop and bucket away without another word.

CHAPTER 10

HOCUS POCUS FOCUS

It had only been about a month, but Tanner had his routine down. As long as he could suck back two sweet-and-light coffees and eat four Werther's hard candies—a supply he was embarrassed to admit he always had on hand—within an hour-and-a-half of his scheduled recording time for his Thursday pick-me-up segment, he'd be satisfactorily "amped" to do it in one take. He'd also feel capable of scaling the exterior of the building when he finished, but that was a whole other story.

Still humming from the enthusiasm, sugar, and caffeine, he left the recording studio and slammed right into Cassie.

"Thankfully, neither of us carrying cups of coffee." Her caramel eyes melted his.

"I'm so sorry." He rubbed the back of his head, feeling for a knot from banging it on the door frame, though it was probably too soon for that. "I wasn't expecting anyone to be here."

"No need to apologize. I'm early. I'm supposed to be recording some commercials for my segments, and I came early to try to get amped up enough."

He reached into his pocket and pulled out a handful of Werther's candies. "These help."

"Wow! I haven't had these since I was a kid. My grandmother used to eat them." Cassie unwound a wrapper.

"Mine got me hooked on them, too." The way she popped the candy into her mouth mesmerized him.

Phil came through a studio door and interrupted them. "Cassie! Great to see you. Just give me a sec to set up, and we'll start recording your commercials."

"Have you done any of these?" she asked Tanner.

He'd been so focused on the candy that he knew was on her tongue, he struggled to understand what she meant.

"Any of what?"

"Ads?"

"They're no harder than a regular segment."

"And candy gets you amped?"

"It helps." Watching her move the candy around her mouth was too much. "Joe!" he shouted, remembering he had wanted to speak to her about him. After the basement chat, he realized he needed to call off the bet. "Can we talk when you're done?"

"Of course."

Once more, he sat at the end of the hall and waited for her. This time, he would have loved for Marley to text him and distract him from his bouncing thoughts. He had started to realize he needed to spend the least amount of time possible close to Cassie. She clearly just wanted a business relationship with him, which was fine. He just needed there to be some distance until he could get over his crush, or whatever this was.

But when she stepped out of the studio, all he wanted to do was be close to her.

"I only needed two takes this time. I think the candy, coupled with the two cups of coffee I had before I started, helped." She grinned. His stomach softened, and he thought of the wilted flowers he'd returned to Marley.

"What did you want to talk about? I'd love to get a cup of coffee, but I don't think I should have any more caffeine today." She started walking, leading him to the front of the building.

"Definitely understand that." She was easy to be with; walking beside her felt like the most natural thing in the world. "But I'd give anything for a pumpkin-spice muffin."

"I know just the place." She paused outside the front door to pull on her cardigan.

"Is that the same one you wore when . . . we first met?" He was standing so close he could smell her perfume—floral with a hint of spice.

"The dry cleaner got the stain out."

"You didn't send me the bill."

"I appreciated the offer, but I was just as much to blame. I wasn't watching where I was going, either." She led him away from the studio, toward the café where Joe worked. "Besides, I'm glad we ran into each other."

"Because of Alice?"

"Well, there's that. But I enjoy your company, too."

What made her say things like that? He was so confused.

He needed a few steps to pull together what he'd wanted to talk to her about. "I was at Joe's place, er, I visited Joe in my sister's basement. And I think we should cancel our bet."

"Given up already?" Cassie smiled. "Are you ready to admit that life coaches can be helpful?"

He realized he didn't know whether or not she was helping Joe. "I guess so. I mean, Joe showed me his binder and talked about the homework you've given him. It all seems great, but he's still a janitor."

"Look—"

"No. Hear me out. It makes me uncomfortable to bet on his life like that. I mean, he's been doing more behind the scenes than I realized. I hadn't given him the benefit of the doubt. I thought he was taking advantage of my sister's generosity. But he's been paying people back and . . . it's just wrong to bet like that about someone's livelihood."

"I totally agree. I wasn't planning on taking your money."

"Really?"

"Really. Helping people is my purpose."

"Regardless of the bet, I think we should pay you for your time."

"I appreciate that." She stopped outside a bakery.

"But I've been trying to shift away from life coaching and focus on the nonprofit. I have a tendency to go overboard and take on more than I should. I don't want anything to suffer because I'm spread too thin. The nonprofit is my focus. I'm going to give up my Monday TV segment, too."

"Why?"

"When I looked at what was motivating me to do them, none of the reasons were the right ones. The best thing that could come from them would be exposure for my nonprofit, but the station doesn't want me to mention it. There's just a blurb about it in my bio on their website. Now that I've stopped taking on more coaching clients, it's just another distraction."

"But you just did a commercial for it."

"I know. I spoke to Phil and told him I'd stay on until they found someone else."

"Well, I'll miss seeing you around there." At least that would help him lessen his contact with her. But he couldn't help but notice how sad that made him feel.

"You'll see me plenty. After all, you're speaking at the career fair, right?"

"Right."

She opened the door of the bakery. "I promised you pumpkin muffins, and these are the best around."

"Wonderful!" He held the door while she entered. "Care to share one?"

"Oh, you'll definitely want it all to yourself." He

could have sworn her eyes sparkled when she laughed. "Besides, I just came by to give the owner some flyers for the career fair. I spoke with her yesterday about selling pastries and coffees that day." She stepped away from him, pulling flyers from her bag. "It was really nice to see you, Tanner."

And with that, she was off, leaving him to eat his muffin alone.

It was so unlike Cassie to have such a terrible yoga session, but she just couldn't get Tanner out of her head. She couldn't focus on the poses. There had been something different about Tanner the last time she'd seen him. She couldn't pinpoint it exactly, but something had definitely felt off. He seemed to go back and forth between being incredibly distant, almost cold, to suddenly like he couldn't get close enough to her. Or was it just that she wanted him to get closer?

As she washed up and changed in the locker room, she tried to shove thoughts about Tanner away from her mind. She did want to be closer to him. But not now. Not until she felt solid with the nonprofit. Maybe after the career fair, she could start thinking about him as more than just a business associate. Though she wasn't sure when their paths would cross again after the fair was over.

"Cassie Davis?" A woman called to her as she left the locker room.

Turning, she recognized a local florist she'd helped when she worked for the city. "Marley, right? Marley O'Keefe?"

"Yes! It's so good to see you again."

Cassie wondered briefly if Marley had been in her yoga class. She inwardly cringed at the tumble she had taken in the middle of her Warrior II pose. "How are you? How is the flower shop?"

"Things are going great." Marley placed her hand on her belly. "Otherwise, I wouldn't be able to be here taking a prenatal yoga class."

"Congratulations! I'm so happy for you. I remember talking about how important your family is to you."

"It is for my brother, too, you know." Marley stepped a little closer, bent her head as if she was about to whisper a conspiracy theory. "He's just reluctant to admit it. It's hard for him to allow people in."

"Your brother?"

"Oh, right. You wouldn't have realized we are related." Marley's good-natured laugh eased Cassie. "My name before I got married was Marley Clark. Tanner Clark is my brother."

"Oh gosh! He said his sister was a florist, but I didn't realize he meant you. What a funny coincidence." Though Cassie now realized Marley and Tanner shared the same smile, although she didn't quite feel the same thing when Marley smiled at her as she did when Tanner smiled her way. "You must give him all your leftover arrangements. He sent one to me and brought me another. Leftovers or not, they were absolutely stunning."

"Wait. He said they were leftovers?" Marley tilted her head.

"Well, no. The tulips were because he spilled coffee on my sweater, but when he brought the others to my office, he just said his sister was a florist. I just assumed . . ."

"Oh, good grief. Who gives someone flowers and doesn't tell them why they're giving them flowers?" She tapped Cassie's arm and looked at the time on her phone. "Just be patient with him. Ever since we lost our parents as kids, he's just had a hard time with commitment. He resists letting people get too close to him, even if he'll never admit that's what's going on. He's sweet and kind but has a lot of walls up, I'm afraid. But I think you'll find a way through. He'll eventually get there."

Cassie wasn't sure how to respond. A flurry of questions ran through her head, but she couldn't force any of them into words.

"I'm so sorry to chat and run, but I have to get going." She took a step away, stopped, and turned. "Oh, the real reason I wanted to stop you was to say thank you. Whatever you're doing with my cousin, Joe? He hasn't been snarling around me and my girls nearly as much lately, and he actually cleaned up the basement."

"Oh, you're welcome," Cassie managed to say as she waved goodbye. She turned to leave the yoga studio. What just happened? So, Tanner was Marley O'Keefe's brother? Memories of working with Marley flooded back. Her story of the loss of her parents, her marriage and children as soon as she was out of school. Marley's face had lit up as she talked about her husband and a house filled with children. She couldn't reconcile Marley with the career-minded, solo Tanner she knew. Clearly, the siblings had approached their adulthood in two very different ways. But what had Marley meant about being patient with Tanner? What was Cassie supposed to be patient about?

CHAPTER 11

HIGH SCHOOL ALL OVER AGAIN

D o school gymnasiums ever smell any different? That certain mix of sweat, old sneakers, and disinfectant. Tanner hadn't liked it when he'd been a student, and he still didn't like it as an adult. Where was Cassie? He couldn't wait to finish and get out of here. He was about midway across the basketball court when he spotted her.

"Hey there!" Cassie called from a side entrance. Micki trailed behind her with a clipboard in her hand. Micki's hair was just barely restrained by three pencils strategically entwined with her curls. "Thank you for stopping by on such short notice. We've got about a half-hour to do a final measure and make sure our plans will work for next Saturday."

"No problem. What do you need from me?"

"Here," Micki handed him the clipboard. "I sketched a floor-plan. We were hoping to set up a make-shift stage for you, but there's just not enough room. It doesn't surprise me. This place is awful—always has been, always will be."

Cassie grimaced at Tanner. "You'll have to excuse her, Tanner. This was our rival high school. Micki's volleyball team lost the state championships to them, and she's never gotten over it."

"Wait. You went to East?"

"We both did," Micki answered.

"I went here. Our girls' volleyball team was amazing. I remember when they won the championship."

"You mean when they got lucky on all those calls and unfairly stole that last set?"

Cassie literally stepped between the two of them. "We're all adults, and that was a really long time ago. Let's just move on. Remember, Micki, West is giving us the use of their gym for next Saturday. We appreciate that so much, right?" She dipped her chin and looked at Micki under raised eyebrows.

Tanner had to hold back the laughter. Cassie would make a great mom. *Where did that thought come from?*

"I had nothing to do with anything on the volleyball court. I wasn't even at that game, Micki. High school sports were not my thing."

"Me neither." Cassie flashed her killer smile at him. "I was on the debate team."

"I did DECA. It's like a marketing kind of club."

"You guys only had to go to school for half the day, right?" Micki asked him.

"During my senior year. Yeah, we all went to a job."

"I remember that. Felt like I was missing out on something. Anyway," Micki pointed to a spot on the floor-plan. "What we can do is pull out one section of bleachers so people can sit in them and listen to you talk. Would you be okay with that?"

"I guess so." "I guess so." He couldn't figure out how the paper translated to the gym, but it didn't matter. He could talk from anywhere.

"Great." Micki took the clipboard and walked away, scribbling something down on it. Tanner heard his cell ding. A quick glance told him it was Marley.

Invite Cassie to Gram's bday 2morrow.

Was she out of her mind?

Mind your own business, he texted back.

Before he could return the phone to his pocket, she replied.

If you have somebody with you, all the aunts can't pester you about getting married.

"Ugh."

"Is everything okay?" Cassie asked him.

"Sorry. Didn't mean to say that out loud." He pointed to his phone. "My sister is a bother sometimes."

"Marley? I ran into her yesterday. I didn't realize she was your sister."

"I'm done, Cass." Micki called from the end of the gym. "You okay if I head out?"

"Of course! Thanks for everything, Micki!"

Marley hadn't mentioned seeing Cassie to Tanner. Although that would explain the suggestion to invite Cassie to their grandmother's birthday. She'd probably spent the entire night struggling to find a way to get Tanner and Cassie together in one place.

"I saw Marley as I was leaving yoga. She was headed in to a prenatal class."

"You do yoga?"

"You sound surprised." She looked offended as they walked out of the gym together.

He found himself noticing again how natural it felt to walk and talk with her. "Not surprised at all. It makes sense because you look amazing." *Did he really say that?* Heat rushed to his cheeks. "I mean, you look healthy, strong. You just always seem so busy. Focused on work, the nonprofit, the career fair, Joe, whatever else you have going on."

She stopped outside the gym and looked at her phone. "I do have a lot going on. But yoga is what keeps me grounded. I'm not sure what I'd be like without it. It's really the only thing that helps me keep the stress level down. Yoga helps me feel like I can actually accomplish all these goals I've given myself—or at least breathe through them."

"Of course you can accomplish them. You're one of the most competent people I've ever met." He touched her arm. "You're so focused."

"Probably too focused?" She seemed to be asking him something, but he wasn't sure how to respond. "Did Joe tell you about what I shared with him? About when I worked for the city?"

A stab of jealousy clenched Tanner's stomach as he

thought about Cassie confiding in Joe. "Joe hasn't told me a thing about what the two of you talk about."

"The city fired me."

"They did?"

"I mean, ultimately, it was the best thing that could have happened to me. If that hadn't happened, I wouldn't have started my coaching business. I wouldn't have found my way to creating the nonprofit. I wouldn't be where I am."

"I hear a 'but' coming."

"But I'm terrified I didn't learn my lesson. I was fired because I was too focused on my ideas being the right ones and not paying attention to the details and how I could manage everything at once. I had too many things going on and didn't have enough support. I keep worrying that I'm making the same mistakes all over again. Like I'm just going overboard and repeating the same failures. Sometimes it feels like the nonprofit, the career fair—it's all just consuming every part of my life. There's nothing left. I couldn't even hold a pose yesterday in yoga. What if I'm just setting myself up to see it all come crashing down again?" She waved a hand toward the gym behind them.

A ding came from Tanner's cell in his pocket. It had to be Marley, again.

"What about trying something different? Spending time doing something just for the fun of it?" He glanced at his phone.

"Should I just invite her for you?" Marley wanted to know.

"Like what?" she asked.

"Well, I know this might sound weird. And feel free to say no." Tanner pinched his nose. He couldn't believe he was about to ask her this. "Sunday afternoon, we'll be celebrating my grandmother's eightieth birthday at her house. Would you like to come with me?"

Cassie's face cracked open in an enormous grin. "Yes, that sounds like fun. My parents moved to Florida, and I haven't been to a family birthday celebration in ages. I'd love to go!"

###

Jayden was waiting outside when Cassie arrived at the café.

"Are you ready?" she asked him.

"I'm nervous." He pulled the door open for her. "My background is fast food. I don't know anything about what they do at a place like this."

"That's the whole point of being mentored," she assured him. "You're not expected to know everything already. You're expected to learn from someone else who knows. They don't expect anything from you but a willingness to learn."

Donna was sitting at a table in the dining area. Cassie waved to her and led Jayden over. She quickly introduced the two. "I'm going to make myself scarce and leave things to the two of you. This is your mentor–mentee relationship, and I'm just the one who brought you together. Jayden, Donna is going to provide feedback to me through weekly updates. That way, if there are any areas she identifies for training or education, we can make sure you have resources for whatever you need."

"Got it," Jayden nodded.

"I'll also expect weekly reports from you, Jayden, on what you're learning and what your experience is."

"Sounds good," he said. And Donna nodded as well.

Back in the kitchen, Cassie found Joe sitting on the crates by the trash bin.

"Supervising?" she asked.

"I'm on break. Nothing else to do. What are you doing here?" He pulled his phone from a pocket. "We aren't scheduled today, are we?"

"No. I just brought someone in for Donna to mentor and thought—"

"You what?"

"I brought a mentee to Donna—"

"That woman doesn't know how to run a restaurant!" He waved his hand as if trying to erase Cassie's words. "Your mentee is going to have a horrible experience, mark my words."

"Joe, that's not fair." Cassie threw her hair behind her shoulder.

"Fair has nothing to do with it. I know how to run a restaurant. She does not."

"Maybe there is more than one way to run a restaurant. Maybe your way isn't the only way?"

He smirked. "Maybe. But have you eaten the food she serves here?"

"I interviewed her extensively, Joe. I wouldn't just assign someone a mentee without knowing the business and the businessperson inside and out. She's been in business for well over five years. Her customers are people who like good coffee—which we both know this place serves—but who also want a healthier option to eat with their coffee. Something different from the typical pastry, doughnut, or baked good. I'm not that customer, and neither are you, but that doesn't mean those customers don't exist. Her business is doing well enough that she's thinking of expanding. That doesn't sound like someone who doesn't know what she's doing."

He jumped off the crates. "My break is over."

"I'm sorry, Joe."

He stood with his back toward her, facing the kitchen. She watched his shoulders raise and lower and assumed he was trying to control whatever emotion he was feeling. She waited.

"Who is this kid who's working with her?" he asked, turning back around.

"Well, he's not a kid. He's a grown man. He was in college on a basketball scholarship, but an injury took him and he can't play anymore. He was working in fast food—"

"Ugh—that's even worse!"

"But he trains as much as he can, and his health is very important to him. He enjoys the restaurant industry and wants to find out more about working somewhere that is focused on healthier options, not so much frying and red meat."

Joe turned around again, reached for his mop and bucket.

"Are you okay, Joe?" Cassie tried to block him from walking away from her.

"I guess I'm just jealous. He's young. He doesn't have as big a hill to climb to make a comeback."

"You're young. You have decades ahead of you. But you just have to control your attitude and focus your energy in the direction of your goals." The vehement tone in her voice surprised her, but she didn't bother trying to walk it back. "What happened? I thought you were making progress."

"My homework happened, remember?" Joe shoved his mop into his bucket, sloshing water over the sides.

"That's why I stopped by today. To see how you were feeling. Still hung up on those same thoughts?"

"You mean the fear of falling on my face? Of being outed as a failure to the entire world all over again?" Joe looked at her as he wiped up the water with the mop. "It wasn't a passing thought. I'm obviously not the kind of guy who can handle success. Why bother trying?"

She watched him clean. He held a similar resem-
blance to Marley and Tanner; she saw it now. But clearly,
the spirit and light in him had been dimmed. "How old
were you when success really hit you? I mean big success.
The moment you realized you were 'making it?'"

"Twenty-seven. I celebrated my birthday that year
with a bunch of people who won't even look at me now.
We had a limo, magnums of champagne . . . "

"Had anyone trained you on how to handle that kind
of success?"

"I don't think that kind of training exists."

"Most people have a chance to mature as an adult
before they reach it. When you're young and everything
happens so rapidly, maybe you need help without even
realizing it."

"What are you saying?" He rested on his mop handle.

"Maybe you're placing the reason for your failure in
the wrong place. You seem to think you're incapable of
being successful—"

"No. I think I'm incapable of maintaining success."

"Whatever. That's still not the reason why you had
a fall."

"Why did I fail?"

"Maybe you were too immature? I was twenty-seven
when I decided to ignore what my supervisors were telling me in the city. I thought I knew it all." She shrugged.
"I didn't. I still don't. But I do know I will never stop

listening to those around me. I'll never get back to that point where I refuse to learn."

He replaced the mop in the bucket and looked around, as if searching for something else to do.

"It's not a matter of being capable. It's a matter of being willing."

He pulled a rag from a pocket and wiped down the rim of the garbage can. Cassie suppressed a smile. Clearly, the man needed more to do.

"If I tell you something, you won't tell anyone, right?" He glanced at her nervously.

"Client confidentiality." She held her hands in the air as if swearing a double oath.

"I want to do what you do. I want to help people, like you do, but with a focus on this kind of stuff." He swirled the rag in the air. "How to run a kitchen, how to manage food prep processes. I should be the one out there talking to that guy. Sure, he wants to do healthy foods, big deal. That's not the important part. He needs to understand inventory management, billing, payroll, forecasting. He needs to understand how, when you're really good at something, people will try to take advantage of you, will try to ride on your coattails, use you up for what they want and then never give you a second thought. You need to be grounded to handle that. You need . . . " He frowned. "Why are you looking at me like that?"

"That's passion, Joe! This is wonderful."

"I feel it. I even explored an online, life-coaching course. I used to be great at working a room, talking to people. Believe it or not, I have some really great people skills. I want to tap back into that."

"I love it!" Cassie clapped her hands. "Why don't you talk to Donna? I'm sure she'd let you spend some time mentoring Jayden."

"Yeah?"

"Of course. Jayden will then have the benefit of learning from both of you."

Joe scratched his chin. "I guess my big test will be Sunday."

"What is Sunday?"

"It's my grandmother's eightieth birthday party. A bunch of nosy aunts, uncles, and cousins—including Tanner—will surround me, all asking me about my future, asking what I'm doing to fix my life."

"And?"

"When I tell them what I want to—that I want to help people bounce back and transform their lives, I know they're going to think I'm a flake. They're going to think it's me wasting time and money all over again."

"How do you know that?"

"They're constantly hounding me. I can tell what they all think."

"Do you know what they think? Or are you assuming what they think?"

"Is there a difference?"

"Definitely. All you owe them is the truth. How they feel about it or react to it is on them. You're not responsible for that. Plus, I'll be there. I'll back you up."

"Why will you be there?"

"Tanner invited me."

"Are you two . . . dating?"

It was Cassie's turn to scratch her head. "Honestly? I'm not exactly sure why he invited me."

CHAPTER 12

SURPRISE!

"Tanner, this is Gloria." Aunt Joann pulled on the arm of a woman until she stood directly in front of Tanner. "I think you two would hit it off beautifully!"

"Oh, thanks Aunt Joann, but—"

"Gloria is the medical assistant at my podiatrist's. She knows all my secrets, but she promised not to tell you any of them, so don't even try it."

The woman gave an awkward laugh, looking absolutely uncomfortable. "It's nice to meet you, Tanner. I've heard all about you." She held out her hand, and Tanner shook it.

"Nice to meet you, too." Tanner felt his smile freeze on his face. *Where was Cassie?*

"I hear you give speeches or something?" Gloria asked.

"Not just speeches, dear. Tanner is a motivational speaker. He's been on YouTube and everything."

"I'm so sorry. I promised Marley I'd help her with something. Will the of you two excuse me?"

Tanner jogged to the kitchen without looking back.

Marley was pulling a tray of shrimp cocktail out of the refrigerator.

"Aunt Joann is trying to fix me up."

"That girl from her podiatrist's office?" Marley snorted. "Good thing Cassie's coming."

"But she's not here yet. Give me something to do."

"Help me set out the hors d'oeuvres in the dining room. Make them look pretty."

"You're kidding. I'm your brother. When is food pretty?"

In the dining room, Tanner placed the shrimp and a tray of mini crab cakes on the table. On his next trip, he put out vegetable egg rolls and a charcuterie tray. The food looked amazing, and he couldn't wait until everyone arrived and they could dig in. He knew his sister didn't prepare all this and wondered who had. He threw "pretty" thoughts and shuffled around an assortment of sauces and trays. Soon, he realized he was no longer alone.

"Look at you over here, busting beads." Gloria placed her hand on his arm and squeezed.

"Busting beads?"

"Working hard! Sweating?" She laughed and tightened her grip. "What exactly are you doing here?"

"Helping my sister set out the food stuff. She wants it to look nice." He pulled his arm from her grasp and shifted a tray of sauce next to the crab cakes.

"Well, I am here to rescue you!" She playfully slapped him on the shoulder and giggled. "Here." She moved the sauce closer to the egg rolls instead.

He glanced toward the front of the house and felt his shoulders suddenly relax as he saw Cassie near the door talking to Joe and their grandmother. He tried to figure out how to politely remove himself from the dining room when Marley saved him.

"Tanner!" Marley called from the kitchen.

"I need to see what else my sister needs."

Before he could turn away from the table, Cassie locked eyes with him, right as Gloria entwined her arm with his and walked with him toward the kitchen.

Cassie suddenly regretted coming. Why would Tanner have invited her here if he had another date? She realized her fingers were shaking as she chatted with Tanner and Joe's grandmother. She tried to focus on Joe and Madeline—it was Madeline's birthday they were celebrating after all, but all she could think of was the woman with her arm linked with Tanner's. Her stomach dropped, and she fought back the burning in her eyes, her throat. She wished there was a way she could excuse herself and leave, but she'd only just arrived.

"I must say, dear," she caught Madeline saying, "whatever you are doing with Joe is just phenomenal. He told me his plans—how he's getting certified to become a life coach."

"I'm so excited for him." Cassie smiled at Joe, fighting

her urge to look for wherever Tanner and his "friend" had disappeared to.

"But it will take some time to get certified. That means a few more weeks in Marley's basement, which I know isn't ideal." Joe stared at the floor.

"Move in with me, dear." Madeline smiled at Joe. "I'd love to have you." It warmed Cassie's heart to see how much she loved her grandson.

"Gram, I wouldn't burden you like that." Joe kissed her cheek.

"No burden at all. I've always wanted a live-in personal chef." She winked at Cassie.

"Hey there!" Tanner approached them—alone, Cassie noted. "I'm so happy to see you!"

"You are?" She looked past him to the woman frowning from across the room.

"Really." Tanner held Cassie's gaze. "It turns out my Aunt Joann didn't know I was bringing a date and had taken the liberty of inviting one for me. From her podiatrist's office."

Joe couldn't help but laugh. "She brought a dental hygienist for me a couple of years ago."

"Let's get you a drink, Cassie?" Tanner touched her arm.

She was still trying to wrap her head around him calling her his date. Was that what she was? "I'd love a drink."

He led her toward the kitchen, and then they took their glasses of wine out to the sun porch at the rear of the house.

"So, here we are." He held his glass to her. "No need for business talk today."

She clinked her glass with his. "I'm really that obnoxious, aren't I?"

"I would never use the word obnoxious."

Cassie smiled. "I hope you don't play poker. You are terrible at bluffing."

He shook his head and laughed. "That definitely seems to be a popular opinion lately. But you're not obnoxious. You're passionate. And I like that." He took a long drink from his glass, waiting to see if she'd respond to that, relieved to see her smile. "I saw you locked in conversation with Gram. What was that about?"

"Oh, that was all Joe. He was telling her all about his plans for the future."

"Really? She looked so happy."

Cassie cocked an eyebrow. "He's decided to become a certified life coach."

Tanner burst out laughing. "Are you serious?"

"I am."

"Well, I guess you win the bet. You convinced him to do something with his life, after all."

"Good thing—"

Suddenly, she realized Joe was on the porch as well, glaring at them both. "That's client confidentiality?"

"Joe! I'm sorry. I assumed since you told your grandmother that it wasn't a secret anymore."

Joe turned toward Tanner. "What did you mean when you said 'bet'? You bet Cassie I couldn't do something with my life?"

Cassie looked at Tanner. How could they explain that there really was no bet now, but at one point there was?

Tanner frowned. "I just wanted to see if Cassie could help you, Joe. Nothing I was saying was sinking in, and I bet her that—"

"And you," he turned to Cassie. "Your line about 'helping people gives me purpose.' I can't believe I fell for that." Joe's face reddened.

"Joe, that was the truth." Cassie stepped toward him. "You don't understand!"

"I understand everything too clearly." He stormed away from the house, leaving Cassie and Tanner alone on the sun porch.

CHAPTER 13

MONDAY FUNDAY

It was Monday morning, and Cassie was definitely not amped about taping her positivity segment. There were so many takes this time that she lost count. Finally, she just let herself speak from the heart. She talked about being vulnerable and admitting when you've done something wrong. She hoped Joe would be watching the morning news. Eventually, she stepped out of the studio closet, disappointed in yet one more thing she'd done poorly.

"That's all right, Cassie," Phil assured her. "Everyone has an off day."

"Good thing you got me, sweetheart!" Gabi roared.

Phil looked at Cassie. "She said you contacted her about your time slot?"

"I did, Phil." Cassie squeezed her forehead while she gathered her thoughts. "Gabi, I thought I told you I'd speak to Phil today. You didn't need to come."

"It's okay!" Gabi nearly shouted. "I got your back, honey! I'm here for *you!*"

"Well, Phil, as you can see, Gabi has plenty of energy to amp that motivation. I bet she will never need more than one take. Her enthusiasm will fire people up."

"You have to light the world on fire—beginning with your own soul!" Gabi announced. "That's what I always say."

Phil grinned. "Well, how are you in front of a camera?"

"Sweetheart! I was born for it."

Cassie nodded a goodbye and headed toward the door.

She was scheduled to meet with Joe at the café, but after yesterday, she wasn't sure if she should expect him to see her. She kept thinking of the look on his face, the way she'd watched as he disappeared on his bike. He hadn't returned any calls or texts from her or Tanner.

She texted Donna: is Joe in today?

Her heart dropped to her stomach when she saw the almost-immediate reply: 'Joe's not welcome here anymore.'

Instead of heading to the café, she went to her office.

Micki covered the mouthpiece of the phone and mouthed "go to your office" as soon as she saw Cassie. Cassie found Joe sitting in the chair across from her desk.

"Thank goodness." Cassie placed a hand on his shoulder. "I'm so glad to see you. Look, you have the wrong idea."

"Then tell me the right idea. So far, you've been nothing but grief for me."

She sat in her chair on the opposite side of her desk.

"Because of you, I got fired today. Was it not enough that you won your bet with Tanner?"

"Listen to me. That's not it at all. My end of the 'bet'

was a silly cup of coffee I'd buy for him if I couldn't help you. And if I did help you, he was going to pay my coaching fees. But we called off the bet a while ago. There was no bet. Yesterday, what you heard was a joke. We are both so happy for you and your new plans for the future. All we wanted was for you to be happy and back on your feet."

He continued to scowl at her for a few breaths before he let himself relax in the chair. "I'm only here because of Gram. When I told her about the bet, she said it didn't make sense. She said that it was out of character for Tanner, and she couldn't imagine someone who helped me so much wasn't sincere. But even if I give you the benefit of the doubt, it doesn't change the fact that I got fired today because of you."

She leaned back in her chair. "Joe, I don't know what happened with Donna, but at some point, you have to take responsibility for yourself."

"I did what you told me!"

"You asked her about helping to mentor Jayden?"

"I told her I could give the kid what he needed."

"That's not the same thing, Joe."

"She said she was tired of my attitude and would rather mop the floors and take out the trash herself."

Cassie collapsed, and her head fell into her hands. "If you're going to be a life coach, you need to work on your delivery." She looked at him.

"Will you mentor me on that?"

"Of course, but . . . "

"And in the interim, can I work for you? I still need a paycheck."

She blew out a puff of air. "I don't have the budget, Joe. Right now we're trying to decide whether to pay an instructor to lead one of our leadership courses or buy actual adult furniture. Once our funding comes through, I might be able to hire you as an instructor for a course on administrative tasks, budgeting, inventory. But I can't hire you now. We need to do more fundraising before we're ready to take on another employee."

"Have you thought about reaching out to local companies to do training for them? They would pay you."

"I don't have the staff."

"You could hire me, and," his voice shifted to a perceptibly lighter tone, "judging by the way he looks at you, Tanner would work for you for free."

She smiled, glad the conversation was taking a shift. "I don't know, Joe. I'm not kidding when I say the budget is tight—"

"I have another ace up my sleeve." Joe leaned over her desk, his head just inches away from hers.

"What do you mean?"

"A few of my recipes qualified as intellectual property—trade secrets. I've been holding onto them as a last resort."

"I don't understand."

"I could sell them. Invest in your nonprofit. Become a part of this."

"I still don't think I understand."

"This is just too much for two people and you know it. That woman," he nodded toward Micki, "is scrambling to hold everything together. I've been here a half-hour and can't believe all that she's juggling. You need another person helping you both. Let me be that person."

"Again, I—"

"If I make the investment and become a partner, we could buy furniture and hire an instructor."

"But—"

"And that means a local restaurant will have access to knowing how to make my zucchini chips."

"Now, you've got a deal." Cassie held out her hand to shake.

CHAPTER 14

No Quitting Here

"I can't believe how well this went today." Cassie stretched out her legs on the bleachers, looking at Tanner next to her.

"I expected nothing less." He put his arm around her shoulders, hesitant only until he felt her lean into him. He relaxed. He could get used to this.

"I can't believe how that man can charm people!" Micki pointed to Joe as he worked the floor, talking to the vendors as they packed up their tables.

"I'm surprised, too," Cassie said.

"I'm not," Tanner chimed in. "Joe can turn on the charisma—when he wants to."

"I guess he just needed to find a reason to want to. Oh, my." Cassie pointed to where Joe was now speaking to Alice Bradshaw. "She looks like she's ready to eat out of his hand."

"I'm going to find out what that's about." Micki headed over.

"Thank you." Tanner whispered the words against the side of Cassie's head.

"For what?" She leaned closer into him, pulling in the minty clean scent of him, feeling more peaceful than she had in weeks, maybe longer.

"For not giving up on him, for one thing."

"I wasn't going to quit."

"And for being here with me." He squeezed her a little tighter and kissed her cheek.

"I don't plan on quitting either."

Epilogue

In *You Don't Get To Quit*, multiple threads are woven into this tapestry of life's scenarios that all ring true to the central theme of the book. Marley expresses a constant sense of frustration and impatience with her cousin, Joe, who was only supposed to live in her basement for a short time, until he got back on his feet. When this arrangement lasts much longer than expected, Marley's patience is pushed to the limit as she attempts to get Joe to move out so she can make room for her soon-to-be-born third child.

But Marley didn't give up on Joe. She encourages her brother, Tanner, to get involved, and through consistent mediation with him and his new acquaintance, Cassie, Joe pulls himself together and gets back on track to meet Marley's pre-delivery deadline. Joe even helps with getting the space ready by assisting Marley's husband.

Tanner was a successful and respected motivational speaker and had no interest in starting a romantic relationship. Then Life Coach Cassie Davis enters his life, and Tanner challenges her to help his cousin, Joe, turn his life around after a disastrous business venture. Tanner is sure Cassie will fail, but she accepts the challenge.

Cassie has challenges of her own: a new spot as a TV-segment host and a new, not-for-profit business. As she juggles these responsibilities, her confidence and self-esteem waiver, and she worries she's taken on too much, just like when she worked as a city manager—and got fired. But Cassie uses her internal motivation and focusing skills and doesn't give up on Joe. She keeps her mind and thoughts positive and successfully inspires Joe to get his life together and make progress toward building a new career. The bonus outcome for Cassie is her unexpected, budding relationship with Tanner Clark, who surprisingly, becomes a welcome distraction from her hectic career. This is a relationship she doesn't plan to quit!

As for Joe, the failed entrepreneur softens-up his attitude and allows Cassie to become his life coach. Though reluctant to take her seriously in the beginning, Joe eventually takes Cassie's feedback to heart, resolves lingering issues from past failures and discovers a renewed sense of purpose and outlook for his life.

I encourage you to read this story again and highlight the positive life-principals designed to fortify your mind and enrich your daily life. May you be inspired to follow your dreams, accept the failures along the way, and never, ever quit!"

> Remember, You Don't Get to Quit.
> Fail, Yes. Quit, Never.

For deeper insights and inspiration, follow Tracey at www.traceypowell.com

About Tracey Powell

Tracey Powell currently works as a technology consultant, helping national and international companies optimize their customer engagement capabilities.

His background includes seventeen years in banking, training as a Special Forces operative, and serving as an associate pastor after attending practical theology school. He holds an MBA from the University of Miami, studied entrepreneurial finance at London Business School, and has been part of multiple, successful start-up companies that have generated millions of dollars in profits for their owners.

An avid traveler, Tracey spent substantial time in Southeast Asia, Southern Africa, and the Caribbean, and conducted multiple excursions into Latin America.

CPSIA information can be obtained
at www.ICGtesting.com
Printed in the USA
BVHW051647260723
667842BV00002B/15

9 798885 810593